THERAPY APPROACHES FOR PERSONS WITH MENTAL RETARDATION

Edited by
Robert J. Fletcher, D.S.W., A.C.S.W.

2000

NADD Press, Kingston, NY

132 Fair Street
Kingston, New York 12401

Library of Congress Number: 99-72057

ISBN 1-57256-010-X

1st Printing 2000

Printed in the United States of America

TABLE OF CONTENTS

SERIES FOREWARD

The books in this series present the newest developments in a specific area of concern. Each book will contain a balance of chapters reporting theoretical formulations, empirical research, clinical procedure and models of service delivery.

The first book in the NADD series, *Assessment and Treatment of Anxiety Disorders in Persons with Mental Retardation* was edited by Ann Poindexter, M.D. This book, *Therapy Approaches with Persons who have Mental Retardation* edited by Robert J. Fletcher, D.S.W., is the second book within the series. The next publication, *Aggression and Other Disruptive-Behavior Disorders in Persons with Developmental Disabilities: Issues and Practices* edited by William I. Gardner, Ph.D., will be published in the near future. Other subject areas currently under preparation for the book series include: program models, psychopharmacology, older adults and staff training.

As series editors, we look forward to a successful series of books that will keep readers informed of advances in knowledge and practice.

Series Editors:

Robert J. Fletcher, D.S.W., A.C.S.W.
Executive Director
NADD
Kingston, New York

William I. Gardner, Ph.D.
Professor Emeritus
Rehabilitation Psychology Program
University of Wisconsin-Madison
Madison, Wisconsin

CONTRIBUTORS

Christine Bellordre
New England Medical Center
Boston, MA

Mary Ann Blotzer, LCSW-C
Private Practice
Bluie, MD

Diane Cox-Lindenbaum, ACSW
Private Practice
Ridgefield, CT

Robert J. Fletcher, DSW, ACSW
NADD
Kingston, NY

William I. Gardner, PhD
University of Wisconsin-Madison
Madison, WI

Stephen Gilson, PhD
Virginia Commonwealth University
Richmond, VA

Anne DesNoyers Hurley, PhD
Tufts University School of Medicine
and New England Medical Center
Boston, MA

Ellen Keller, PsyD
Young Adult Institute
New York, NY

Lark Kirchner, LCSW
Southern Illinois University
Springfield, IL

Andrew Levitas, MD
University of Medicine and Dentistry
of New Jersey
Stratford, NJ

Louis Lindenbaum, EdD
Putnam ARC
Carmel, NY

Melanie Mueth, MD
Southern Illinois University
Springfield, IL

Richard Ruth, PhD
Private Practice
Wheaton, MD

Daniel J. Tomasulo, PhD, TEP, CGP
Private Practice
Holmdel, NJ

INTRODUCTION

Robert J. Fletcher, D.S.W., A.C.S.W.

Over the past few years, psychotherapy has gained increased acceptance in the professional community as a suitable form of treatment for persons who have developmental disabilities. The goals of psychotherapy with this group are no different than those used within the general population. The intended outcome of therapy is a change of one's thoughts, feelings, and/or behaviors. A variety of theoretical orientations and techniques has been adapted for use with persons with intellectual disabilities.

This book is a compilation of chapters that deals with various therapy approaches for persons who have an intellectual disability. The purpose of this book is to foster an understanding of therapeutic techniques that assist this particular population in becoming more productive at home and in society. Topics include behavioral and cognitive behavioral therapy interventions, issues of transference and counter-transference, the dynamics of group, family and individual therapies, treatment of suicidal ideation and providing psychotherapy for the sex offender.

William I. Gardner, Ph.D. provides an in-depth understanding of selecting and implementing the best behavioral therapy for those with developmental disabilities in his chapter "Behavioral Therapies: Using Diagnostic Formulations to Individualize Treatment for Persons with Developmental Disabilities". He asserts that the conditions must be changed that cause maladaptive behaviors, and that these conditions influence behavioral symptoms. Previously, it was popular to use psychotropic medications and employ behavioral modification in an attempt to suppress the undesired symptoms. This method has been largely unsuccessful in treating and changing the conditions that influence the maladaptive behaviors in persons with developmental disabilities. Gardner notes that "the behavior therapy approach recognizes the reciprocal interdependence of behaviors, emotions and cognitions" and that the "goals of therapeutic interventions are to change these instigating, vulnerable, and maintaining conditions rather than to modify or eliminate the symptoms". The selection of treatment for the individual is guided by pretreatment assessment. Oftentimes the client is unaware of the motivational forces or instigating influences that precede challenging behaviors. "The behavior therapy approach, following identification of the instigating conditions, would seek to provide those therapeutic experiences designed to teach personal recognition of these controlling antecedents, along with those that systematically teach alternative coping and personal accountability skills." Gardner's chapter focuses on the present emotional and behavioral states of clients. Questions therapists should ask include "What is happening with the client now, and why?"

Ellen M. Keller, Psy.D. in her chapter "Points of Intervention: Facilitating the Process of Psychotherapy with People who have Developmental Disabilities" addresses issues of establishing effective therapeutic relationships in psychotherapy and how to best understand and anticipate certain pitfalls that occur during the therapeutic process (such as misreading the communication skills of a client, issues of privacy, confidentiality, involvement of significant others in treatment and termination of therapy). Dr. Keller provides case examples that demonstrate the effectiveness of her techniques as well as the positive and favorable results that occur when the therapeutic process has been explained to her clients. She further outlines the complicated and difficult process of providing psychotherapy to individuals with disabilities. Establishing clear boundaries, educating involved parties, ensuring that newly acquired skills and behaviors will be reinforced by service providers and/or significant others are some of the specific areas covered in her chapter.

Preconceived attitudes and beliefs of professionals who work with people who have developmental disabilities often undermine the patient's true capabilities. Levitas and Gilson explore the issues of "Transference and Counter-transference in Individual Psychotherapy" with persons who are developmentally disabled. In order to facilitate the most effective working relationship between therapist and client, ground rules must be laid. It is important to establish the understanding factor within this delicate relationship. It should be made clear to the patient at the onset of therapy that if he/she does not understand certain questions or directives, he/she must make the counselor aware of this fact. Gathering as much background information as possible is integral to treating those with developmental disabilities. "All sources of history should be explored" to best understand where the client is coming from emotionally and developmentally. The authors recommend interviewing persons at both home and school in order to have access to possible sources of helpful information, as well as the awareness of the therapist of the developmental conditions of adolescents who are developmentally disabled and their ways of interpersonally relating.

Contrary to popular belief, group therapy among persons with developmental disabilities is most effective in helping these individuals understand the complexities they face, the cognitive and developmental milestones they must reach and the highest level of functioning they can attain in society. Daniel Tomasulo, Ph.D. in his chapter "Group Therapy for People with Mental Retardation" dispels the widely held view that people with mental retardation cannot benefit from group therapy because of their developmental disabilities. To ensure that therapy is effective, Dr. Tomasulo has developed an Interactive Behavior Group Therapy Model (IBT) which incorporates cognitive networking whereby members repeat what other group members say. This therapeutic technique demonstrates that the person speaking has been heard, acknowledged and supported by the other group members. He claims that interaction of this type is paramount for the establishment of a successful group dynamic. In his chapter he shows how to establish a group dynamic, how to hold a "warm up" session (which prepares group members for what is to come), and how to maximize the group members' potentials and levels of functioning within the group and in society.

Another pitfall to which therapists in the field succumb is the "Egocentric Error". Mary Ann Blotzer, L.C.S.W.-C. encourages therapists to step out of their own state of egocentricity and into the phenomenological world of their clients. Empathy, understanding and objectivity are key elements to effective therapy with this population of individuals. She explains in her chapter how easy it is for therapists to impose their personal biases and prejudices on to the client. Another professional hazard which besets therapists who deal with persons who have developmental disabilities is stereotyping. She claims this is extremely dangerous in that each client is an individual and has his/her own needs. Oftentimes therapists become "stuck" with a particular client and feelings of boredom can hinder progress. Her prescription for this predicament is continued empathy for the client and to view this period of boredom and frustration as a tool for learning about the therapist's own counter transferential reactions.

"The Inner Life and the Outer World in Treating Persons with Mental Retardation" by Richard Ruth, Ph.D. shows how the psychoanalytic approach can be most beneficial in providing a bridge of understanding between the inner world and outer reality of persons with mental retardation. His chapter focuses on the alienation suffered by those who have a disability and the obstacles the therapist must overcome in understanding the connection between the behavior and the inner workings (or "voice") of the individual. Dr. Ruth believes that interpreting behavior is more important than controlling behavior; moreover, it is important for the patient to think about his/her behavior. It is the job of the therapist to foster this understanding and way of thinking within his/her client.

Another type of group therapy that is integral to the support of the developmentally disabled individual is family therapy. "Family Therapy" by Louis Lindenbaum, Ed.D. states that it is essential for parents of persons with developmental disabilities to receive professional counseling throughout the various stages of their child's development in order to understand their issues of having a child who has mental retardation. The challenge rests not only with the developmentally disabled child but with his/her family as well. "The ultimate goal is to empower family members to take responsibility for their own lives." In the past, families were seen by those in the mental health field as being hindrances to the child's progress rather than being helpful. Thanks to continued writings by those like Dr. Lindenbaum, this narrow and shallow view is starting to change.

Suicide is defined in Kaplan, Sadock & Greeb (1994) as "intentional self-inflicted death...a way out of a problem or a crisis that is invariably causing intense suffering" (p.803). This intense suffering is precisely that which requires the attention of professionals and those who work with suicidal individuals.

Suicide ideation, attempts, and completion occur in people with developmental disabilities at various functional and intellectual levels.

In order for psychotherapy to be most beneficial to those who have developmental disabilities and are repeat sex offenders, a "new self" concept must be established within the client for whom treatment is being sought. Diane Cox-Lindenbaum, A.C.S.W. explores the bureaucratic difficulties that abound when attempting to reach this population of sex offenders in her chapter titled "Psychotherapy for Sex Offenders". She states that a majority of problems stem from the various agencies "passing the buck" which leaves the developmentally disabled person without a stable source of help and support. She advocates group therapy for managing the deviant behavior of sex offenders and that this type of therapy is most successful. Ms. Cox-Lindenbaum puts forth a model of treatment for these individuals based on group interaction. Her therapeutic techniques include a contract among group participants, the use of feeling logs, relaxation training, personalized stress reduction plans and relapse prevention and social skill training. She claims that social skill retraining is imperative in overcoming aberrant sexual behavior because inappropriate behavior is usually a mask that covers up personal inadequacies within the individual.

The various therapeutic approaches as outlined in this book are designed to assist those who work with or live with those who have developmental disabilities. We hope to provide a better understanding into the therapeutic, cognitive and emotional world of persons who have developmental disabilities. These techniques and approaches have proved to be effective and successful with persons who have mental retardation. Each client needs to be assessed and treated with his/her individual needs in focus. We hope this book is helpful in determining and assessing those needs of persons who have mental retardation and mental health concerns.

Individual, group or family psychotherapy can be effective approaches in meeting the mental health needs of individuals, their families and other supportive resources involved within the life of the individual. This book is intended to provide the reader with an understanding of how treatment modalities and techniques can be implemented in providing therapy for persons who have developmental disabilities. The principles, clinical skills, knowledge and values that have been effectively demonstrated within the general population have proven useful in treating individuals who have developmental disabilities.

CHAPTER ONE

BEHAVIORAL THERAPIES: USING DIAGNOSTIC FORMULATION TO INDIVIDUALIZE TREATMENT FOR PERSONS WITH DEVELOPMENTAL DISABILITIES AND MENTAL HEALTH CONCERNS

William I. Gardner, Ph.D.

Contemporary behavior therapies represent a diverse group of clinical assessment and treatment procedures derived from reinforcement (operant), emotional (respondent), observational (modeling, social), cognitive, self-regulatory and related theoretical models of human functioning. *Applied behavior analysis, behavior management, behavior modification, behavior therapy, behavioral treatment, cognitive-behavior therapy, contingency management, emotional retraining, panic control treatment, problem solving, reinforcement therapy, self-control therapy, self-management training,* and *social skills training* are among the terms used by various writers, either to refer to specific groups of approaches or as generic labels to encompass a broader range of behavior therapy procedures and their major conceptual foundations (Bellack & Hersen, 1993; Craighead, Craighead, Kazdin, & Mahoney, 1994; O'Donohue & Krasner, 1995).

A central assumption underlying behavior therapy procedures is that current behavioral and emotional difficulties to a major extent reflect the effects of past and present faulty or deficient learning experiences. The behavior therapies are used to offset the effects of these experiences by changing *instigating*, *vulnerability*, and *maintaining* influences currently present within the person and/or within the person's physical and social environments (Bellack & Hersen, 1993; Gardner, 1988; Griffiths, Gardner, & Nugent, 1998; O'Donohue & Krasner, 1995). The end goal is one of *increasing the person's competencies* and in so doing both to reduce or eliminate current behavioral and emotional symptoms and to reduce the risk of their recurrence. To accomplish these objectives with a specific client, the behavior therapist selects from an array of available ones those therapy procedures that hold promise of effectively addressing current conditions identified during individualized assessment as contributing to the person's difficulties (Nezu & Nezu, 1995). As detailed in later sections, this selection is guided by a set of diagnostic formulations derived from a study of the multiple specific personal and environmental contexts of the person's presenting problems (Gardner, 1998; Gardner, Graeber, & Cole, 1996; Gardner & Sovner, 1994).

As examples of the range of behavior therapy procedures available for use in this selection process, a therapist may choose on the basis of client-specific diagnostic formulations of conditions influencing current symptoms: (a) *systematic desensitization and related stimulus exposure procedures* (respondent-based learning paradigm) to eliminate clinically significant fears and obsessive-compulsive behaviors for some clients (Erfanian & Miltenberger, 1990; Hiss & Kozak, 1991), (b) *a skills training program* (operant-based learning paradigm) to teach alternative functional communication skills to replace self-injurious and aggressive symptoms (Bird, Dores, Moniz, & Robinson, 1989; Carr et al., 1994; Durand, 1990), or for other clients to teach behaviors incompatible with phobic behaviors relating to animals (Arnatzen & Almas, 1997), (c) *a social skills program* (operant and social learning paradigms) to teach prosocial interpersonal skills as alternatives to aggressive and other disruptive responding of adults with a dual diagnosis of mental disorders and mental retardation (Foxx, McMorrow, & Schloss, 1983; Matson & Stephens, 1978), (d) *a self-management program* (social learning and cognitive-behavioral paradigms) to teach coping alternatives to multiple behavioral and emotional symptoms for clients with chronic and severe behavior disorders (Benson, 1992; Cole, Gardner, & Karan, 1985; Jackson & Altman, 1996; Koegel, Koegel, & Parks, 1990; Reese, Sherman, & Sheldon, 1984), or (e) *cognitive-behavioral programs* for reducing depression in young adults (Lindsay, Howells, & Pitcaithly, 1993) or for eliminating exhibitionism in adult males with mild cognitive impairment convicted of indecent exposure (Lindsay, Marshall, Neilson, Quinn, & Smith, 1998). Primary sources that provide more comprehensive descriptions of these and related applications to persons with mental retardation include Cipani (1989); Gardner & Cole, (1993); Gardner & Sovner, (1994); Griffiths et al., (1998); Jacobson & Mulick, (1996); Luiselli & Cameron, (1998); Matson & Barrett,(1993); Nezu, Nezu, & Gill-Weiss, (1992); and Thompson & Gray, (1994).

This chapter illustrates this *process of selecting therapy procedures* based on individually derived diagnostic formulations relating to conditions that influence occurrence, severity, fluctuation, and persistence of target symptoms. The reader will note that this treatment selection process differs significantly from that followed in contrasting psychological treatment paradigms identified as intrapsychic in focus and based on such approaches as psychoanalytic theory, Gestalt theory, self theory, and other psychodynamic views of personality structure and abnormality. In these and similarly oriented explanatory systems, treatment approaches most typically are predetermined to address specific presumed sources of psychopathology. As a result, the same basic treatment is provided to all clients. To illustrate, in psychoanalytic therapy unconscious motivations become a major focus of treatment. In self-theory, faulty self-image becomes the focus of treatment. To the extent that the nature of treatment is predetermined, pretreatment assessment is not as critical to the treatment selection process. As noted by Craighead et al. (1994), in these treatment paradigms:

> The problems that clients express are reformulated in terms of personality or characterological defects, deficits, inabilities, or deeply rooted causes. The labels imply a permanent, complex psychological state that is not readily alterable. Behavioral problems are attributed to defects in personality or psychological development. The defects are considered to be deeply rooted, making treatment an extremely elaborate endeavor (p. 21).

Biomedical and Psychosocial Influences

Prior to discussion of a behavior analytic approach for gaining the needed assessment information for selecting treatment procedures, the potential interactive effects of biomedical and psychosocial influences on behavioral and emotional symptoms are explored. Although the current chapter is devoted to behavior therapy, these therapeutic procedures should be closely interfaced with biomedical diagnostic and intervention formulations to insure maximum therapeutic effects.

Historically, behavioral and emotional symptoms presented by those with mental retardation have been viewed predominately from either a biomedical or a behavioral perspective, with the frequent result that behaviorally-responsive symptoms/disorders were "medicalized" and treated with behavior-altering medications and biomedically-responsive symptoms/disorders were "behavioralized" and treated with behavior modification procedures. These early behavioral procedures focused primarily on reducing or eliminating problem behaviors and only infrequently attempted either to change the conditions producing the behavior or to teach functional prosocial alternatives to these. As a result, the overuse of psychotropic medications and the misuse of behavioral procedures to suppress symptoms in the absence of a diagnostic understanding of the specific and frequently multiple factors influencing symptom presentation were a typical result. Although more recent models of treatment focus have moved in the direction of integrating these different approaches (Pyles, Muniz, Cade, & Sivla, 1997; Sturmey, 1995), these have not articulated the particular roles or relative influences assumed by biomedical or psychosocial conditions in producing the behavioral and emotional symptoms.

Dissatisfaction with this separatist approach led to the development of an integrative multimodal contextual behavior analytic alternative to diagnosis and treatment selection. This alternative reflects a biopsychosocial view of human behavior in that it emphasizes that behavioral and emotional difficulties represent the influences of a person with psychological and biomedical, including psychiatric and neuropsychiatric, characteristics as he/she interacts with physical and psychosocial environments (Gardner et al., 1996; Gardner & Sovner, 1994; Gardner & Whalen, 1996; Griffiths et al., 1998).

To illustrate the reciprocal interdependence of these multiple influences, chemically-based psychiatric conditions such as schizophrenia or a bipolar disorder may result in changes in cognitive functions, mood and affective states, emotional regulation, and psychomotor behaviors. These changing psychological and physical characteristics may influence occurrence of new behavioral or emotional difficulties or may contribute to occurrence or increased severity of problems that predated a current psychiatric episode (Lowery & Sovner, 1991). These symptoms in turn create more than usual changes in the manner in which the social environment responds to and interacts with the person and his/her problem behaviors. These experiences with the social environment may in a reciprocal manner strengthen the problem behaviors or intensify the emotional arousal and the person's perceptions of the social feedback. An effective treatment program must be responsive to these reciprocal interrelationships and provide attention to each set of influences (Gardner & Sovner, 1994; Griffiths et al.). In such instances, to insure optimal effectiveness and sensitivity to the integrity of the person, behavior therapy procedures should be interfaced closely with biomedical interventions.

A Look Ahead

As background for discussion of a diagnostic model to guide the treatment selection process, some of the major assumptions and psychological principles that guide the behavior therapy assessment and treatment process are described.

Nature of Maladaptive Symptoms

The majority of psychological problems presented by individuals with mental retardation and treated by the behavior therapist are predominately of an overt *behavioral* presentation. Due to the excessive and disruptive nature of these, difficulties are created both for the person and those in the person's social environments. Examples include verbal and physical aggression, excessive disruptive activity level, sexually inappropriate acts, impulsive agitated/disruptive episodes, ritualistic/compulsive routines, property damage or destruction, self-injury, and stereotypy. This behavioral presentation is illustrated as follows:

> Ms. Susan Fuhrer, a woman with moderate cognitive and adaptive behavior impairments and a medical diagnosis of Down Syndrome, recently was placed in a foster home following a period of residing in a group home. In this setting, Ms. Fuhrer continued to present chronic problems of verbal and physical aggression toward peers and staff, episodes of self-abuse, frequent property destruction, occasional threats and attempts at elopement, frequent uncooperativeness, and frequent refusals to attend and participate in her day program.

Other psychological problems presented by persons with developmental disabilities have a predominant *emotional* presentation. These include such concerns as excessive fearfulness, specific phobias, dysphoric mood, excessive anger, specific and generalized anxiety, and general irritability. While frequently not as socially disruptive or visible, these problems with predominate emotional components when unrecognized and untreated may contribute significantly to the person's general adaptive inadequacy and detract from the individual's general quality of life. Ms. Katherine Gray illustrates psychological problems having major emotional components:

> Ms. Gray, a young woman with moderate cognitive impairment, recently graduated from a special education program located in a small school district. Shortly thereafter, she moved with her parents to a large city in another state and was enrolled in a vocational program providing supported employment services. Although she had never used public transportation, she now was expected to ride the city buses to her job placement. Throughout her high school program, Ms. Gray had been one of a circle of peers who depended on one another for social support. In her new location, she found herself without a familiar group of peers. In fact, in her job placement she was one of only two persons with cognitive disabilities among a large group of employees. Additionally, her two sisters and their families with whom she previously had spent the majority of her leisure time were no longer available. In this new setting, Ms. Gray gradually began to isolate herself from others and refused to use public transportation. She seldom talked except in response to direct questions, lost interest in her usual leisure activities, appeared sad most of the time, began to experience sleep and appetite problems, and would cry and withdraw from social interaction when prompted to "get involved" by parents when at home or by staff when in her vocational program. After a period of unacceptable performance, she was terminated from her job placement.

Even in persons whose major difficulties are of an emotional nature, it is not unusual for these psychological features to contribute to an increased likelihood of overt behavioral symptoms such as aggression or hyperactivity. Mr. Travis Ferguson illustrates this relationship:

> Mr. Ferguson becomes noticeably anxious and irritable whenever his ritualistic routine is disrupted. When prompted by staff or peers to engage in behavior inconsistent with his usual routine, Mr. Ferguson frequently becomes verbally and physically aggressive. In this instance, his state of negative emotional arousal increased the likelihood of agitated/disruptive behaviors. On other occasions when not anxious and irritable, he is most pleasant and cooperative. Effective behavior therapy treatment of the aggressive episodes would involve attention to the affective arousal as a major antecedent influence.

These vignettes emphasize that the presenting symptoms, when viewed in isolation, do not provide valuable diagnostic information about the causes of these symptoms and thus offer minimal direction to therapy selection. Gardner (1996) has suggested that these psychological concerns be viewed as "nonspecific symptoms" because when viewed in isolation these are not specific to any cause or set of causes but rather may be influenced in occurrence and severity by a variety of conditions. The term "symptom" is used to emphasize that any problem of a psychological nature, whether predominantly behavioral or emotional, is a "symptom of," that is, the end result of or produced by some other conditions. The primary target of behavior therapy thus *must be these other conditions* that produce the symptoms rather than the symptoms themselves. To emphasize, Mr. Ferguson's aggression would not represent the direct target of behavior therapy interventions. The therapist must "look beyond" the symptomatic aggressive behavior and seek to identify, and change or eliminate, the conditions that influence occurrence of these acts. If the aggression is managed or controlled directly, it is likely to occur again as the personal aberrant conditions of significance to its occurrence have not been modified or eliminated.

Historical vs. Functional Views of Causation

The behavior therapist approaches the question of explanation of current behavioral and emotional symptoms (e.g., "Why does Mr. Jensen display such intense temper outbursts?") from both *developmental* (historical) and *functional* (contemporary) viewpoints. From a *developmental* perspective, recurring problems are viewed as resulting from a biologically and experientially unique person as he or she previously has interacted with social and physical environments. It is assumed that a person's current behavioral and emotional difficulties represent the end result of a complex learning history whose effects have accumulated to provide both the *"form"* of current problems and the *"meanings"* or influences that certain environmental and internal events or conditions have on instigating and on changing the future strength of these problems. At any given time in the past, any specific experience may have exerted only a minute influence on the development, maintenance, or modification of various problem behaviors and emotions. But an increasing number of such experiences may have had the cumulative effects of producing a strong response tendency to engage in argumentative, highly anxious, and aggressive actions. In contrast, other more appropriate experiences may have resulted in behaviors of a cooperative, attentive, and socially engaging nature.

To illustrate this perspective, an adult with mental retardation with chronic excessive fear of social contact may engage in a panic attack in a crowded grocery store. This incident would be viewed as representing "the end point of the interaction of genetic constitutional factors, the current physiological state of the individual, his current environmental conditions, and past learning, which in turn, was a function of a similar interaction" (Ross & Ross, 1982, p. 6). The physiological components of this cluster of influencing events refer to the person's total physical characteristics.

As noted by Bijou (1972), atypical biological factors may limit a person's response equipment - his or her sensory, motor, and/or neurological connecting systems and thus interfere with or reduce his or her normal response potential. Or these may provide an abnormal internal environment, so that the stimulation usually present is either absent or occurs with higher than usual intensity or duration. Under these conditions, atypical reactions may occur, as when a person is over reactive to minor distractions. In the case of sensory and muscular handicaps, the person may be limited in the types and intensities of stimulation to which she or he may be receptive and to the type of responses that she or he can make. Again, the person's current behavior, typical or atypical, reflects the historical influence of these individually unique physical states or conditions. In view of the frequent occurrence of physical abnormalities in persons with mental retardation, such factors must be considered in attempts to understand the development of behavioral and emotional symptoms.

It is recognized, nonetheless, that problem behavior patterns that appear to be the cumulative influence of physical factors may partially reflect psychological influences. As such, these may respond positively to behavior therapy approaches. In illustration, some persons with central nervous system impairment and mental retardation may be prone to exhibit hyperactivity, impulsivity, and attentional problems. It may be possible to obtain improvement in these problem areas through use of behavior therapy procedures (Alabiso, 1975; Dubros & Daniels, 1966). As a second example, persons with mental retardation and various medical disorders, such as Lesch-Nyhan Syndrome, have a tendency to demonstrate severe and chronic episodes of self-injurious behaviors, such as biting the tongue, lips and fingers, face slapping, and head banging. Various behavior therapy procedures have been found valuable in reducing the severity and chronicity of severe self-mutilation in some instances, even though the major controlling conditions in development and continuation of these behaviors appear to be physical in nature (Flavell, 1982).

To summarize this discussion of historical causation, even though the behavior therapist focuses on behavioral and emotional symptoms as these occur in the *present* social and physical environments, it is recognized that these personal characteristics are rooted in earlier experiences of the person. In fact, to the extent that present problems can be viewed as learned actions, prior learning is a given.

As the focus of assessment and intervention activities is on *current* conditions that influence *current* personal problem behaviors, speculation about the developmental history is of value only to the extent that it satisfies one's curiosity about the types of learning experiences whose effects have accumulated to give *form* and *meaning* to present controlling conditions. As treatment is focused on these *current* conditions, the critical analysis involves identification of current external and internal conditions that presently influence occurrence, magnitude, variability, and persistence of these problem features. Such diagnostic information provides a *contemporary or functional* explanation. To emphasize, in seeking to understand a person's presenting symptoms, the major pre-intervention diagnostic focus of the behavior therapist is that of developing a contemporary or functional explanation derived from a comprehensive analysis of the current multiple contexts of current presenting symptoms.

In this diagnostic process, care is taken to distinguish *description* from *explanation*. It may be observed that an adolescent's episodes of verbal and physical aggression is accompanied by an agitated state of anger. It might be tempting to suggest, "He fights because he is angry," thus using a description of one characteristic as an explanation for another. Being angry may indeed be one of the conditions that increase the likelihood of fighting, but anger would not be viewed as an adequate explanation of the behavior. The behavior therapist would identify other *preceding instigating events* or *conditions* (e.g., teased by a physically smaller peer; reprimanded by staff when in an irritable emotional state), *consequences* (e.g., the aggressive acts may be a functional means of terminating the teasing), and, of considerable significance, *personal vulnerability features* (e.g., the adolescent has limited alternative skills of coping with his anger or limited conflict resolution skills for negotiating a reduction or termination of the teasing) as a basis for development of a more useful complex of interrelated explanations and related therapeutic interventions.

Normality vs. Abnormality

The behavior therapist views behavioral and emotional symptoms as reflecting the same learning and related principles that are involved in the development and maintenance of more desirable characteristics. With this view, behavioral and emotional difficulties of persons with mental retardation are assumed to result from the person's previous experiences and reflect current conditions. As noted earlier, the current influences of physical factors are recognized as a component of current experiences.

There is no assumption of a *discontinuity* between normal and problem characteristics, that is, that normal behaviors and emotions result from one set of principles and "abnormal" or "pathological" behaviors and emotions from a different set of psychological principles. To illustrate, highly aggressive, overactive, and disruptive behaviors of an adolescent with mental retardation in home and school would not be viewed as reflecting a set of principles that differ from those used to account for his socially appropriate behaviors. Rather, the behavior therapist assumes that both sets of behaviors reflect the same basic underlying principles of behavior development and expression.

In devising a historical explanation of behavioral and emotional concerns, it is assumed that the social and physical environments in which these have developed provided inappropriate or "abnormal" experiences for the adolescent. These experiences, rather than the person or the behavioral and emotional expressions, are viewed as abnormal, as these have created or contributed to the person's current problems. As an example, if the adolescent were exposed to frequent and intense abusive outbursts from an ill-tempered adult, intense and pervasive negative behavioral and emotional reactions would be expected. The behavior therapy model would not view the person's behaviors as abnormal. The negative emotionality displayed by the person would not be viewed as abnormal. The psychological principles underlying the acquisition and expression of the negative emotions would not be viewed as abnormal. Rather, the environmental experiences to which the person had been exposed would represent the abnormal variable in the development of the debilitating behavioral and emotional reactions. To emphasize, the problem behaviors and emotions represent the *normal* outcome of *abnormal* experiences.

The implication of this view of abnormality is both obvious and of considerable importance to the behavior therapist. The nature and scope of diagnostic activities, the interpretation of assessment information gained, the relationship between assessment results and related intervention formulations, the specific therapy procedures selected, and the focus of interventions are all influenced by this view.

This view of the nature of abnormality also emphasizes that the particular abnormal influences on symptoms most typically vary considerably from person to person. Similar challenging behaviors such as chronically occurring aggression, dysphoric mood, sexually inappropriate acts, social withdrawal, chronic anxiety, or self-injury may reflect quite different previous developmental experiences and, as a result, divergent current personal and social-environmental influences. The therapeutic interventions for similar behavioral and emotional concerns thus *may differ considerably* across individuals based on outcome of an assessment of current and individually-relevant controlling influences.

Functional Feature of Behavioral Symptoms

Behavioral symptoms do not occur randomly or haphazardly. Rather, these behaviors are selective, functional, and purposeful in that these occur only when certain instigating conditions are present. A behavior such as aggression does not occur continuously. Rather, a person behaves aggressively only under certain conditions of instigation such as when taunted by peers or when repeatedly directed by staff to engage in activities that the person does not like. The conditions that serve to signal occurrence of specific challenging behaviors may represent a wide range of biomedical, psychological, and/or socioenvironmental conditions.

These antecedent conditions gain instigating influence or control over behavioral symptoms as these represent signals to the person that specific challenging behaviors will produce specific reinforcing effects or consequences that is, will produce positive consequences and/or will remove, reduce or avoid currently present or anticipated negative conditions. After experiencing this sequence of Antecedents - Behavior - reinforcing Consequences (ABC sequence) on a few occasions, the behavioral symptoms become functional for the person, that is, serve the function or purpose of producing these effects.

When exposed to various antecedents, a person with developmental disabilities and mental health concerns, as noted, may be at increased risk or vulnerable to engage in the behavioral symptoms rather than other acceptable coping behaviors due to various personal and environmental deficits (e.g., coping skill deficits; communication skill deficits; limited program stimulation) and/or pathological features (e.g., allergies that produce psychological distress during pollen season; chronic schizophrenia that occasionally results in delusional thoughts). To illustrate this latter personal feature:

> Mr. Braddock may become aggressive toward staff members who insist that he attend meals during times that he has the delusional belief that the food is poisoned. The aggressive behavior under these conditions may become functional in terminating the staff directive that he attend meals. Mr. Braddock enjoys his meals when he is free of this psychotic symptom.

> Modification of the deficits and pathologies that place the person at increased risk for engaging in challenging behaviors becomes a major program focus of behavior therapy. In the example of Mr. Braddock, medication for the delusional thoughts may be provided. Following successful intervention, the delusional view of food as posing a danger to his health would be eliminated as would his aggressive behaviors following prompts by staff to attend meals. This challenging behavior would become nonfunctional in the absence of the delusional belief as Mr. Braddock would no longer be motivated to avoid "poisoned" food.

Even though behavioral symptoms become functional in producing specific reinforcing effects, it should not be assumed that the person is aware of or knows how the behaviors became attached to antecedent instigating conditions or that these symptoms represent intentional or planned acts. The reinforcing effects of various consequences occur automatically, and frequently are beyond the person's awareness that such habits as aggression, self-injury, property destruction, or tantrumming have come under the influence of certain antecedent instigating events. When a person is asked following occurrence of socially inappropriate acts, "Why did you destroy your roommate's tape?" or "Why did you hit Jon in the face?" a common reply is "I don't know." The person on most occasions is not being evasive in this reply as most challenging behaviors are developed slowly over a period of time during which the behaviors have resulted in reinforcing consequences. With each reinforcing experience, as noted, the preceding behavior gains strength and becomes more habitual or automatic on future exposure to similar antecedent instigating conditions. Thus, behavior may appear to be beyond the control of the person, impulsive, or automatic in nature. In view of this, the behavior therapy approach, following identification of the instigating conditions, would seek to provide those therapeutic experiences designed to teach personal recognition of these controlling antecedents, along with those that systematically teach alternative coping and personal accountability skills.

Focus of Behavior Therapy

In general, behavior therapies are designed to:

- remove or minimize psychosocial influences presumed to instigate and strengthen behavioral and emotional symptoms,
- teach prosocial alternatives as adaptive functionally-equivalent replacements for the behavioral and emotional symptoms, i.e., alternatives that would satisfy the same personal needs or motivations maintaining the symptoms,
- increase the person's motivation to use these newly acquired prosocial skills as functional replacements, and

- reduce or eliminate psychological and socioenvironmental features that serve as risk factors in influencing occurrence and continuation of behavioral and emotional symptoms. In some instances, this may involve changing the motivational basis for symptom occurrence if assessment results suggest that the motivational conditions are abnormal in kind, frequency, intensity or duration. In illustration, assessment may indicate that a high level of anger serves as the motivational basis for a range of verbal and physical aggressive behaviors. In this instance, therapy goals in addition to teaching alternative means of expressing anger would also address means of reducing the excessive nature of the person's anger. In other instances in which the motivation for the behavioral symptoms would be pathological, the therapy goal would be one of eliminating these intervention features. This is illustrated by a person who gains enjoyment out of harming animals, setting fires, or having violent sexual contact with children.

As noted, these goals are accomplished through addressing the factors presumed to influence occurrence and persistence of the symptoms. An adult who displays temper tantrums in his home is taught both to "control his temper" under the specific conditions of provocation and to express his emotions in a more socially and personally enhancing manner. If a child is physically aggressive to peers whenever she becomes jealous of the attention provided by the teacher, and as a result is isolated by peers, behavior therapies would be selected to teach the child alternative socially appropriate and personally enhancing skills of relating both to her feelings and to her peers (Gardner & Moffatt, 1990).

Fourteen-year-old Susanne illustrates this therapy focus:

> Susanne engages in numerous episodes of physical and verbal aggression in both school and home settings. During assessment, a variety of experiences were identified that produced such negative emotional reactions as anger, sadness, loneliness, disappointment, or embarrassment. When experiencing these irritable emotional states, a range of minor aggravations such as teasing by peers, instructions from teachers and parents, and delay in immediate access to desired activities or events resulted in aggressive outbursts. It thus appeared that a range of emotional states when combined with specific sources of aggravation, influenced occurrence of a common reaction of aggression. Susanne was at risk for responding aggressively as she had not learned to respond differentially to different emotions. With this information, the behavior therapy program was designed to teach Susanne (a) to recognize and label different emotions, (b) to relate these different emotions to the differing precipitating conditions, and (c) to use a variety of self-managed socially appropriate behaviors to replace the undifferentiated aggressive reaction.

Roles of Behavior Therapist

The behavior therapist assumes a variety of roles in relating to the problems presented by persons with mental retardation. As the behavior therapy approach views behavioral and emotional difficulties as reflecting the effects of current experiences within a person's physical and social environments as these interact with psychological and physical features of the person, one major therapist role becomes that of changing these daily experiences. If a child is experiencing difficulty in the home, the child-in-the-family may become the focus of treatment, with the therapist providing programmatic direction to rearranging various relationships. If an adolescent is having difficulties in *school* and *home,* family and school members as they interact with the adolescent may become the focus of treatment. If an adult's difficulties in relating to peers in her vocational training program is diagnosed as reflecting the person's shy and passive demeanor, the person's peers, work supervisor, and counselor may be used to assume major therapeutic roles in encouraging a more confident and outgoing demeanor.

In essence, various therapeutic roles may be assumed, under the direction of the behavior therapist, by parents, teachers, counselors, siblings, and others in the person's daily living environments and relationships. As a result, the person and the relevant social environments change in a mutually beneficial manner. Again, the behavior therapist, based on assessment information, provides direction to the types of learning experiences provided by others in the client's natural environments. The reader may refer to Carr et al. (1994), Gardner and Cole (1989) and Gardner et al. (1996) for a range of illustrations of this behavior therapist role.

In other instances, the behavior therapist may indeed work directly with the client in a structured setting/relationship apart from the person's day-to-day world. This may involve facilitating changes, as illustrations, in specific social, anger management, cognitive, conflict resolution, relaxation, self-management, visual imagery, or communication skills that the client may use on future occasions which set the occasion for problem emotions and behaviors. The reader is encouraged to refer to Bensen (1992), Hurley and Silka (1998), Lindsay and Baty (1989), Lindsay et al. (1993) and Lindsay et al. (1998) for illustrations of this therapist role in addressing such problems as anger, anxiety, cognitive distortions, depression, and panic states.

In order to insure generalization from the therapy location and conditions to locations and conditions present in the real world, systematic attention is given to generalization strategies (Griffiths, Feldman, & Tough, 1997). Additionally, specific attention is given to insuring that the new emotional and behavioral skills acquired in therapy are sufficiently valued by the person to insure that these will be used under future real world occasions (Gardner, 1998). Finally, attention is given to insuring that those in the real world will recognize and provide positive feedback for new ways of behaving (Carr et al., 1994).

Psychological Triad

A closely related feature of the behavior therapy approach to treatment selection is recognition of the interactive influence of various psychological features of a person. Although a person's behavioral symptoms such as aggression or self-injury frequently are those that create most concern to the person's social environment, the behavior therapy approach recognizes the reciprocal interdependence of behaviors, emotions, and cognitions. To illustrate, a person's overt behavior (e.g., physical aggression) may influence his or her feelings (e.g., anger, anxiety) and cognitions (e.g., "he deserved that") just as the person's feelings and/or cognitions may influence his or her behaviors. And, each may influence or be influenced by current environmental and biological conditions.

Behavior therapy interventions may be directed toward changing any one or each of these interacting psychological components as a means of reducing the clinical problem. As described by Benson (1992) and Schloss, Smith, Santora, and Bryant (1989), if a person's behavioral symptoms are influenced by anger arousal, the focus of behavior therapy may become one of teaching the person to control or reduce his anger and, as a result, reduce the likelihood of aggressive behavior. If a person engages in repetitive thoughts that a co-worker is dangerous and attempting to harm him, these cognitions may contribute to aggressive acts whenever provoked by the co-worker. Modification of the ruminative thinking through cognitive-behavioral therapy may remove critical instigating conditions for the aggressive acts. A decrease in aggression would be expected (Gardner, Clees, & Cole, 1983). If a person's exhibitionism is influenced by the faulty cognitive assumption (e.g., "She wants me to do it. She enjoys it."), changing the cognition to a more realistic one may influence more socially appropriate interpersonal behavior (Lindsay et al., 1998). Finally, a person's aggressive behaviors may be followed immediately by self-delivery of negative consequences. These experiences may result in inhibition of future impulses for aggressive acts, changes in the person's cognitions (e.g., "I'll not hit him because I'll lose my bonus"), and a reduction in the level of anger, which in turn may result in a decease in aggressive responding (Cole et al., 1985).

In sum, regardless of the specific type or focus of behavior therapy, it is recognized that each component of a person's psychological triad (behaviors, emotions, cognitions) may be influenced. Thus, psychological, or medical when addressing biomedically related influences, intervention efforts address one or a combination of these interactive conditions identified during assessment as critical in influencing symptom occurrence (Gardner & Whalen, 1996; Gardner, 1998; Sovner & Hurley, 1992).

Case Formulation Process

With this background, the remaining discussion focuses on the process of case formulation as a basis for evolving a set of diagnostic-intervention formulations that guide the therapy selection process. As noted, the behavior therapy approach places considerable emphasis on this process of looking beyond the challenging behaviors and gathering information to assist in developing a set of person-specific diagnostic-intervention formulations. If these formulations are not thoroughly and accurately completed, specific interventions are likely at best to be ineffective and could in fact be counter-therapeutic.

As there is no single or simple psychological or biomedical mechanism that underlies emotional and behavioral symptoms, a diagnostic assessment includes evaluation of the various personal and environmental contexts in which these occur, viz., (a) the *complete antecedent stimulus complex* that serves to instigate these symptoms, (b) the person's *vulnerabilities or risk factors* for engaging in these symptoms when confronted with the instigating stimulus complex, as well as (c) those *proximate consequences* that follow behavioral occurrences and contribute to their functionality and strength. In developing an understanding of a person's symptoms as a basis for selecting person-specific behavior therapy interventions, a set of diagnostic speculations evolve from the following case formulation process. This case formulation process offers a map for the behavior therapist to follow from the initial step of defining a behavioral or emotional symptom through the final step of evaluating the effectiveness of the therapeutic experiences provided.

In this case formulation process of selecting client-specific interventions, the initial step is to determine what is happening and why, that is, to develop *diagnostic formulations, hypotheses, or hunches After* devising these *diagnostic formulations* about why the symptoms are occurring, a set of diagnostically-based *intervention formulations*, as suggested earlier, is developed. Following implementation of the interventions, results of an evaluation of the effectiveness of these may result in changes in the initial diagnostic formulation and/or in the interventions selected. The case formulation process involves the following:

- **Step 1**: Describing the behavioral and emotional symptoms. The case formulation process is continued only if it is determined that the symptoms are having a significant negative impact on the person's quality of life, are threatening the well being of the person or others, and/or if the person seeks assistance in modifying these symptoms,

- **Step 2:** Gathering diagnostic information through assessment of these symptoms in the contexts of *instigating*, *vulnerability*, and *maintaining* conditions,

- **Step 3:** Forming hunches (hypotheses) about the current medical, psychological, and social-environmental "causes" of specific symptoms, i.e., developing *diagnostic formulations,*

- **Step 4:** Describing specific therapy objectives relative to the "causes" identified in Step 3 as well as specifying the ultimate outcomes of successfully addressing these causes,

- **Step 5:** Developing a set of *intervention formulations* that address the hypothesized "causes" of the challenging behaviors,

- **Step 6:** Selecting an integrated set of client-specific interventions based on specific diagnostic-intervention formulations. To illustrate the difference between this step and the previous one, assume that assessment of a person's disruptive episodes in a group home setting results in a diagnostic hypothesis that this challenging behavior is maintained by the resulting valued staff and peer attention (Step 3). This diagnostic formulation leads to the logically related intervention formulation "meet the person's need for attention in a proactive manner as a means of removing the motivation for the challenging behavior" (Step 5). This general intervention strategy would next be translated into specific approaches such as, (a) minimize attention following disruptive behaviors, (b) provide social attention following a range of prosocial behaviors that the person currently exhibits, (c) provide frequent noncontingent personal attention, (d) teach appropriate ways of soliciting attention, and (e) enrich the person's opportunities for positive social interactions,

- **Step 7:** Developing a *staging* plan for providing the various interventions, i.e., deciding on what interventions should be implemented initially and the sequence or timing of the remaining interventions,

- **Step 8:** Devising and implementing procedures for evaluation of the effectiveness of interventions, and

- **Step 9:** Modifying diagnostic hypotheses and/or interventions based on evaluation results. This step continues until program objectives are met.

Understanding Symptoms In Their Various Contexts

After definition, the next step in the *case formulation process* involves gathering diagnostic information through assessment of the symptoms in the contexts of *instigating*, *vulnerability*, and *reinforcing* conditions. The Multimodal Contextual Behavior Analytic Worksheet presented in Figure 1 depicts these three areas of assessment

		Context 1: Instigating Conditions		Context 2: Vulnerability Conditions	Context 3: Reinforcing Conditions	
		Triggering	Contributing		Positive	Negative
Environmental	Physical					
	Social					
	Program					
Psychological	Present Features					
	Deficit Skills/ Features					
Medical						
Psychiatric/ Neuropsychiatric						

Figure 1: Multimodal Contextual Behavior Analytic Worksheet

Contextual Analysis: Instigating Conditions. The initial diagnostic task is that of placing the symptoms in the contexts of current external (e.g., specific task demands, reduced social attention) and internal (e.g., anxiety, anger, paranoid ideation, repetitive thoughts) stimulus conditions that contribute to the instigation of the behavioral and emotional symptoms. These conditions serve to initiate a specific episode or occurrence of the symptoms of concern (Gardner, 1998).

Contextual Analysis 2: Vulnerability Influences. Observations relating to instigating conditions are combined with those describing relevant personal characteristics (e.g., sensory impairments, anger management skills, borderline personality disorder, mood disorders, communication or coping skills) and socioenvironmental or ecological features (e.g., opportunity for social interaction, type and frequency of structured program activities) that by their absence, low strength, infrequency of occurrence, or pathological nature may contribute to a person's symptoms. These are viewed as *vulnerability* influences as these place the person at increased risk for demonstrating the symptoms under previously identified conditions of instigation. To elaborate, these vulnerabilities increase the risk of aberrant responding in those persons inclined to use such actions to cope with external or internal instigating conditions. No functionally equivalent prosocial alternative personal features may be present in the person's repertoire or, if present, may not be as effective or efficient as the behavioral symptoms in meeting the person's current needs (Horner & Day, 1991). Thus, when attempting to understand and program for a person's symptoms, knowledge of these vulnerability conditions (deficit and pathology areas) guides the clinician in simultaneously pinpointing specific functionally equivalent coping skills and related cognitive, emotional, and motivational supports that will be required for continued successful social and interpersonal functioning following termination of an intervention program (Carr et al., 1994).

Individuals with developmental disabilities present skill deficits in a number of critical areas. Such skill deficits may increase a person's *risk of* displaying behavioral and emotional symptoms. The absence of or limited ability to perform certain skills may result in the person being unable to cope positively with conditions of instigation. To illustrate:

> Consider a man who frequently becomes physically aggressive when taunted by another man in his vocational program. He may lack the skills to select socially acceptable ways of dealing with his tormentor. Lacking these skills, he resorts to aggression, which in turn temporarily stops the teasing. If alternative coping skills are taught and relevant cognitive and motivational changes are facilitated, he is more likely to respond appropriately to the taunting.

Certain skill deficits consistently appear as major vulnerabilities in persons with a developmental disability. Some examples are lack of ability to problem solve, limited anger or anxiety management skills, limited or nonexistent verbal communication skills, low tolerance for stress, and limited social, vocational, and leisure skills (Benson, 1992; Griffiths et al.).

To illustrate, persons with developmental disabilities may use challenging behaviors that usually are not associated with communication to inform us what they need or want. A person may become aggressive whenever he has a headache and is directed to engage in an activity that involves a noisy and crowded setting. Someone else may occasionally become self-injurious to escape from a disliked peer. If communication skills are absent, or if others do not attend to the person's verbal communication, the person may learn to use challenging behavior to get needs met (Carr et al., 1994).

In addition to skill deficits that increase the person's risk of challenging behavior under various conditions of provocation, various personality characteristics and motivational features may represent vulnerabilities. A person may have a personality trait of suspiciousness that, under certain social conditions, may result in misinterpretation of the intent of a peer who offers to share his bag of chips. If the peer persists in his attempts to be charitable, aggressive behavior may result.

Motivational features of a person may represent distinct vulnerabilities. Examples of these for persons with mental health concerns include:

- Numerous aspects of the social and physical environment may represent cues for negative emotional arousal,
- A restricted range of activities, objects, and events present that have positive reinforcement value,
- Specific activities, persons, or objects are excessively sought after or excessively avoided and serve as the major source of motivation for the person's behavior,
- Immediate reinforcement may be required to motivate and maintain prosocial behaviors, and
- Excessive dependence on others to provide reinforcement.

A major focus of *the behavior therapy approach* is on reducing the psychological vulnerabilities identified during assessment.

Contextual Analysis 3: Maintaining Conditions. Given the instigating stimulus conditions and vulnerability influences, the final focus of the contextual analysis is identification of the purposes or functions being served by the symptoms (e.g., terminate aversive demands, modulate pain, decrease unpleasant internal arousal, insure physical contact and other social feedback). These contingent consequences strengthen the symptoms and account for the repeated occurrence of these under future similar instigating and vulnerability influences.

How Factors Interact

Typically, a number of factors interact to influence occurrence, fluctuation, severity, and persistence of behavioral and emotional symptoms: To illustrate:

> Mr. Fontaine's concern about losing his girl friend results in a state of angry agitation. At this time, staff in his group home may begin to insist that he "hurry and get dressed because the group is leaving for the ball game in 5 minutes." Mr. Fontaine is in no mood to accompany the group but is informed that he must go with the group as there is no available staff to remain with him. This increases his agitation level. One of his peers begins to push him toward the bus which produces an aggressive reaction. Finally, one of the staff decides that Mr. Fontaine is too upset to go and remains at home with him.
>
> In assessing "why" the aggressive behavior occurred, several factors must be considered:
>
> worry ➤ angry agitation (*contributing event*) + push from peer (*triggering event*) + limited anger management skills and related coping behaviors (*vulnerabilities*) = aggressive responding ➤ removal of directive to go with the group (*reinforcing consequence*).

Diagnostically-Based Treatment Formulations

These diagnostic hunches about triggering and contributing instigating conditions, relevant vulnerabilities, and the functionality of the symptoms form the basis for formulation of diagnostically-based interventions addressing each of the presumed contributing influences. As noted, major therapeutic efforts are designed to (a) remove or minimize biomedical and psychosocial instigating and maintaining conditions, (b) minimize related vulnerabilities, and (c) reduce or eliminate pathological biomedical conditions and impoverished and abusive features of the social and physical environments that place the person at continued risk. These efforts may include teaching prosocial coping alternatives and increasing the personal motivation to use these newly acquired behavioral, cognitive, and emotional skills as adaptive functional replacements for the maladaptive symptoms. A skill enhancement program focus to offset psychological vulnerabilities is especially pertinent for persons with highly restricted repertoires of coping behaviors. In this personal context, aberrant symptoms may represent highly effective and efficient functional characteristics and must be replaced by equally effective and efficient functionally equivalent coping skills if the symptoms are to be minimized or eliminated (Gardner & Sovner, 1994; Lowery & Sovner, 1991; Sovner & Hurley, 1992).

Figure 2 (page 22) offers a format for integrating the behavior therapy diagnostic-intervention formulations with those, when relevant, of a biomedical nature.

In this integration, the staging plan becomes critical, i.e., deciding which interventions should be implemented initially and the sequence or timing of the remaining interventions. Staging decision are based on consideration of (a) presumed magnitude of influence of specific interventions, (b) the need to sequentially present interventions that build on each other (i.e., the extent to which the effects of any specific intervention is dependent on the effects of earlier interventions), (c) the desirability of determining the separate effects of different interventions, especially those that are intrusive or represent some risk to the physical or psychological well-being of the person, and (d) the projected time period in which treatment effects should be realized. In order to evaluate the effects of specific interventions, it may be necessary to initiate only one intervention at any given time. After determining the effects of this intervention, it may be continued, deleted if found ineffective, or other interventions added to address other instigating, vulnerability, or maintaining influences.

Summary

The behavior therapies represent a diverse group of clinical assessment and treatment procedures derived from various learning and related conceptual models of human functioning. The specific procedures selected for use with a particular client are based on a set of diagnostic formulations relating to conditions presumed to contribute to the occurrence, severity, variability, and persistence of the target symptoms. As such, the goals of therapeutic interventions are to change these instigating, vulnerability, and maintaining conditions rather than to modify or eliminate the symptoms. A case formulation process provides direction to selection and evaluation of these client-specific diagnostically-based interventions.

Multimodal Integrated Intervention Plan

Name: ____________________
Date: ____________________
Staff: ____________________

Target Symptoms

1. ____________________
2. ____________________
3. ____________________

	(A) Diagnostic Hypotheses	(B) Program Objectives	(C) Diagnostically-Based Interventions	(D) Staging Plan	(E) Expected Change (Type/Magnitude/ Time)	(F) Data (Type/Schedule)	(G) Responsible Staff; Review Schedule
Environmental Formulations							
Psychological Formulations							
Medical Formulations							
Psychiatric Formulations							

Figure 2: Multimodal Integrated Intervention Plan Format

References

Alabiso, F. (1975). Operant control of attentional behavior. A treatment for hyperactivity. *Behavior Therapy, 6,* 39-42.

Arnatzen, E., & Almas, I. K. (1997). Reduction of phobic behavior for animals in a boy with mental retardation. *Scandinavian Journal of Behavior Therapy, 26*, 124-131.

Bellack, A. S., & Hersen, M. (Eds.). (1993). *Handbook of behavior therapy in the psychiatric setting*. New York: Plenum.

Benson, B. A. (1992). *Teaching anger management to persons with mental retardation*. Worthington, OH: International Diagnostic Systems.

Bijou, S. W. (1972). Behavior modification in teaching the retarded child. In C.E. Thoresen (Ed.), *The seventy-second yearbook of the national society for the study of education, Part I-Behavior modification in education* (pp. 115-136). Chicago: University of Chicago Press.

Bird, F., Dores, P. A., Moniz, D., & Robinson, J. (1989). Reducing severe aggressive and self-injurious behaviors with functional communication training. *American Journal of Mental Retardation, 94,* 37-48.

Carr, E. G., Levin, L., McConnachie, G., Carlson, J., Kemp, D., & Smith, C. E. (1994). *Communication-based intervention for problem behavior*. Baltimore: Brookes.

Cipani. E. (Ed.). (1989). *The treatment of severe behavior disorders*. Washington, DC: American Association on Mental Retardation.

Cole, C. L., Gardner, W. I., & Karan, O. C. (1985). Self-management training of mentally retarded adults presenting severe conduct difficulties. *Applied Research in Mental Retardation, 6,* 337-347.

Craighead, L. W., Craighead, W. E., Kazdin, A. E., & Mahoney, M. J. (1994). *Cognitive and behavioral interventions.* Needham Heights, MA: Allyn & Bacon.

Dubros, S. G., & Daniels, G. J. (1966). An experimental approach to the reduction of overactive behavior. *Behavior Research and Therapy, 4,* 251-258.

Durand, V. M. (1990). *Severe behavior problems: A functional communication training approach.* New York: Guilford.

Erfanian, N., & Miltenberger, R. G. (1990). Brief report: Contact desensitization in the treatment of dog phobias in persons who have mental retardation. *Behavioral Residential Treatment, 5,* 55-60.

Flavell, J. E. (1982). The treatment of self-injurious behavior. *Behavior Therapy, 13*, 529-554.

Foxx, R. M., McMorrow, M. J., & Schloss, C. N. (1983). Stacking the deck: Teaching social skills to retarded adults with a modified table game. *Journal of Applied Behavior Analysis, 16,* 157-170.

Gardner, W. I. (1998). Creating preventive and proactive interventions. In D.M. Griffiths, W. I. Gardner, & J. Nugent (Eds.), *Behavior supports: Individual centered interventions* (pp. 77-97). Kingston, NY: NADD Press.

Gardner, W. I. (1996). Nonspecific behavioral symptoms in persons with a dual diagnosis: A psychological model for integrating biomedical and psychosocial diagnoses and interventions. *Psychology in Mental Retardation and Developmental Disabilities, 21,* 6-11.

Gardner, W. I. (1988). Behavior therapies: Past, present, and future. In J. A. Stark, F. J. Menolascino, M. H. Albarelli, & D. Gray (Eds.), *Mental retardation and mental health: Classification, diagnosis, treatment, services* (pp. 161-172). New York: Springer-Verlag.

Gardner, W. I., & Cole, C. L. (1993). Aggression and related conduct disorders: Definition, assessment, treatment. In J. L. Matson & R. P. Barrett (Eds.), *Psychopathology in the mentally retarded* (pp. 213-252). Boston: Allyn & Bacon.

Gardner, W. I., & Cole, C. L. (1989). Self-management approaches. In E. Cipani (Ed.), *The treatment of severe behavior disorders: Behavior analysis approaches* (pp. 19-35). Washington, DC: American Association on Mental Retardation.

Gardner, W. I., & Moffatt, C. W. (1990). Aggressive behavior: Definition, assessment, treatment. *International Review of Psychiatry, 2,* 91-100.

Gardner, W. I., & Sovner, R. (1994). *Self-injurious behaviors: Diagnosis and treatment.* Willow Street, PA: Vida.

Gardner, W. I., & Whalen, J. P. (1996). A multi-modal behavior analytic model for evaluating the effects of medical problems on nonspecific behavioral symptoms in persons with developmental disabilities. *Behavioral Interventions: Theory and Practice in Residential and Community-Based Clinical Programs, 11*, 147-161.

Gardner, W. I., Clees, T., & Cole, C. L. (1983). Self-management of disruptive verbal ruminations by a mentally retarded adult. *Applied Research in Mental Retardation, 4,* 41-58.

Gardner, W. I., Graeber, J. L., & Cole, C. L. (1996). Behavior therapies: A multimodal diagnostic and intervention model. In J. W. Jacobson & J. A. Mulick (Eds.), *Manual of diagnosis and professional practice in mental retardation* (pp. 355-370). Washington, DC: American Psychological Association.

Griffiths, D. M., Feldman, M. A., & Tough, S. (1997). Programming generalization of social skills in adults with developmental disabilities: Effects of generalization and social validity. *Behavior Therapy, 28,* 253-269.

Griffiths, D. M., Gardner, W. I., & Nugent. J. (1998). *Behavioral supports: Individual centered behavioral interventions.* Kingston, NY: NADD Press.

Hiss, H., & Kozak, M. J. (1991). Exposure treatment of obsessive-compulsive disorders in the mentally retarded. *The Behavior Therapist, 14,* 163-167.

Horner, R. H., & Day, H. M. (1991). The effects of response efficiency on functionally equivalent competing behaviors. *Journal of Applied Behavior Analysis, 24,* 719-732.

Hurley, A. D., & Silka, V. R. (1998). Cognitive-behavioral treatment for panic disorder. *Mental Health Aspects of Developmental Disabilities, 1,* 119-123.

Jackson, T. L., & Altman, R. (1996). Self-management of aggression in an adult male with mental retardation and severe behavior disorders. *Education and Training in Mental Retardation and Developmental Disabilities, 30,* 55-65.

Jacobson, J. W., & Mulick, J. J. (Eds.). (1996). *Manual of diagnosis and professional practice in mental retardation.* Washington, DC: American Psychological Association.

Koegel, L. K., Koegel, R. L., & Parks, D. R. (1990). *How to teach self-management to people with severe disabilities: A training manual.* Washington, D.C: U.S. Department of Education, Office of Educational Research and Improvement, Educational Resources Information Center.

Lindsay, W. R., & Baty, F. J. (1989). Group relaxation training with adults who are mentally handicapped. *Behavioral Psychotherapy, 17,* 43-51.

Lindsay, W. R., Howells, L., & Pitcaithly, D. (1993). Cognitive therapy for depression with individuals with intellectual disabilities. *British Journal of Medical Psychology, 66,* 135-141.

Lindsay, W. R., Marshall, I., Neilson, C., Quinn, K., & Smith. A. H. W. (1998). The treatment of a learning disability convicted of exhibitionism. *Research in Developmental Disabilities, 19,* 295-316.

Lowery, M. A., & Sovner, R. (1991). Severe behavior problems associated with rapid cycling bipolar disorder in two adults with profound mental retardation. *Journal Intellectual Disability Research, 36,* 269-281.

Luiselli, J. K., & Cameron, M. J. (Eds.). (1998). *Antecedent control: Innovative approaches to behavioral support.* Baltimore: Paul H. Brookes.

Matson. J. L., & Barrett, R. P. (Eds.). (1993). *Psychopathology in the mentally retarded.* Boston: Allyn & Bacon.

Matson, J. L., & Stephens, R. M. (1978). Increasing appropriate behaviors of explosive chronic psychiatric patients with a social skills training package. *Behavior Modification, 2,* 61-76.

Nezu, C. M., & Nezu, A. M. (1995). Clinical decision making in everyday practice: The science in the art. *Cognitive and Behavioral Practice, 2,* 5-25.

Nezu, C. M., Nezu, A. M., & Gill-Weiss M. J. (1992). *Psychopathology in persons with mental retardation: Clinical guidelines for assessment and treatment.* Champaign, IL: Research Press.

O'Donohue, W. O., & Krasner, L. (Eds.). (1995). *Theories of behavior therapy: Exploring behavior change.* Washington, DC: American Psychological Association.

Pyles, D. A., Muniz, K., Cade, A., & Sivla, R. (1997). A behavioral diagnostic paradigm for integrating behavior-analytic and psycho-pharmacological interventions for people with a dual diagnosis. *Research in Developmental Disabilities, 18,* 185-214.

Reese, R. M., Sherman, J. A., & Sheldon, J. (1984). Reducing agitated-disruptive behavior of mentally retarded residents of community group homes: The roles of self-recording and peer-prompted self-recording. *Analysis and Intervention in Developmental Disabilities, 4,* 91-108.

Ross, D. M., & Ross, S. A. (1982). *Hyperactivity* (2nd ed.). New York: Wiley.

Schloss, P. J., Smith, M., Santora, C., & Bryant, R. (1989). A respondent conditioning approach to reducing anger responses of a dually diagnosed man with mild mental retardation. *Behavior Therapy, 20,* 459-464.

Sovner, R., & Hurley, A. (1992). The diagnostic treatment formulation for psychotropic drug therapy. *The Habilitative Mental Healthcare Newsletter, 11,* 81-86.

Sturmey, P. (1995). Diagnostic-based pharmacological treatment of behavior disorders in persons with developmental disabilities: A review and a decision-making typology. *Research in Developmental Disabilities, 16,* 235-252.

Thompson, T., & Gray, D. B. (Eds.). (1994). *Destructive behavior in developmental disabilities: Diagnosis and treatment.* Thousand Oaks, CA: Sage.

CHAPTER TWO

POINTS OF INTERVENTION: FACILITATING THE PROCESS OF PSYCHOTHERAPY WITH PEOPLE WHO HAVE DEVELOPMENTAL DISABILITIES

Ellen M. Keller, Psy.D.

Introduction

The process of providing psychotherapy to people with developmental disabilities is inherently more complex than trying to achieve the same goals with a group of individuals who are not disabled. Not only do difficulties emerge as a direct result of cognitive impairment, but problems also arise from contextual factors. When left unaddressed these may seriously undermine the impact of therapeutic interventions. Strategies that proactively target these factors can greatly enhance the likelihood that therapy will be successful. There are several predictable points in time where the therapist can intervene in order to increase the efficacy of psychotherapy: at the time of referral, during the initial phase of therapy, when new skills are introduced, and when considering termination. While the task of the therapist is different at each juncture, each task is linked by a need to address two common factors: the intrusion of outside forces into a private relationship, and the difficulties that the person with developmental disabilities brings into the therapeutic relationship.

What causes a person to seek out the help of a professional? Typically people present for psychotherapy for one of three reasons: when an individual is experiencing emotional distress, dysfunction in a major life area (i.e., work, family), or pressure from others in their environment. Most people self refer. The exact opposite is true for people with disabilities. People with disabilities are usually referred for mental health services because of disruptive behaviors that interfere with the referring provider's ability to serve that person in the community. Medication (treatment) or behavior modification are the most frequent responses, with the implied goal being the elimination of maladaptive behavior. Even though the communication theory of problem behavior (Carr et al., 1994) is well accepted, behaviors which result in a mental health referral are rarely interpreted in the context of emotional expression. As a result, when psychotherapy is included as an intervention there continues to be an overwhelming emphasis on changing the disruptive behavior (Kroese, 1997).

Clearly, people with disabilities begin therapy differently than their nondisabled counterparts. Another striking difference in the experience of those who are disabled is the involvement of many people in various aspects of the therapeutic process. An important aspect of psychotherapy is privacy. Consider how issues of confidentiality impact on a person's willingness to participate in therapy. Roback and Shelton (1995) report most therapy patients withhold information because they fear negative consequences in their environment (e.g., workplace, home) as a result of breaches in confidentiality. This phenomenon may be even more extreme in the case of working with people with disabilities. Because individuals with disabilities are embedded in multiple service delivery systems, opportunities for privacy are rare.

Breaches in confidentiality often occur between the therapist and the service provider. Confidentiality is most frequently compromised under several conditions:

1) Referring organizations are required to maintain records that document the individual receiving services and the progress made or challenges to be faced.
2) Service providers routinely intrude upon the privacy of people with disabilities and may not be sensitive to maintaining boundaries.
3) Lines of communication between the therapist and service provider neglect privacy needs.

Breakdowns in privacy severely hinder the development of trust; moreover, this breakdown undermines the establishment of a therapeutic relationship. The quality of the therapeutic relationship is not an incidental aspect of the therapeutic process. In fact, it is often the quality of that relationship and not a therapeutic technique that predicts successful outcomes in psychotherapy. Educating involved parties, establishing boundaries, and developing lines of communication between the therapist and other involved parties at the onset of treatment can minimize potential negative consequences arising from the involvement of multiple people in a primarily private process.

Once a person is actively engaged in therapy, the task of the therapist turns to establishing and working towards identified goals. There are several obstacles which have the potential to interfere with this process. First, because of deficits in communication skills, the person with disabilities can easily be excluded from the process of selecting goals. Typically the person who refers the individual to therapy will describe what the goals should be (based upon their knowledge of the person) and may actually be the one to decide whether or not therapy is useful and should be continued. At times, the goals of the person and referring service provider are in conflict (Levitas & Gilson, 1997). For example, the individual may need to exercise greater personal control while the referring service provider emphasizes compliance with rules.

Even when persons with disabilities possess sufficient verbal skills to communicate their desired goals, they often do not understand the purpose of therapy. As a result they have difficulty articulating their own goals. People with disabilities may not understand how therapy is different from other helping relationships and what can realistically be accomplished by engaging in therapy because of the multitude of helpers in their environment. They may assume that the rules that apply to other helping relationships (freely shared information, focus on immediate needs and problem solving, and consequences for appropriate and inappropriate behavior) apply to their relationship with a therapist. As a result, they can become locked in a pattern of discussing day to day activities, reporting problems, and looking to the therapist to provide an immediate solution to concrete concerns. Taking the time to educate persons with disabilities about the nature and purpose of psychotherapy can facilitate their involvement in the therapeutic process.

Kroese (1997) indicated that cognitive distortions, particularly those associated with learned helplessness may interfere with the individual feeling empowered to make changes once goals are collaboratively identified (p. 4). Many of these feelings are deeply rooted in reality. This population comes to therapy with a long history of failure and has few choices with regard to where they live, work, and with whom they socialize. Learned helplessness and feelings of inadequacy need to be addressed in order for goals to be worked on productively (Szymanski & Rosefskey, 1980).

Once therapeutic goals are met, the issue of termination must be addressed. Most professionals agree that the termination phase in psychotherapy must be processed and understood by the individual receiving services in order for termination to be successful. The issue of when to end therapy is more complex when working with people who are disabled. People with disabilities face challenges when ending therapy for several reasons. First, they often have difficulty incorporating new skills into their daily lives, as well as maintaining them (Matson & Gardner, 1991). Skills must be practiced frequently under a variety of applied circumstances in order to be learned. The therapeutic setting is removed from the natural environment and accommodations must be made in order to ensure that the newly acquired skills are successfully introduced into their daily lives. Second, important tasks of termination (such as increasing independence and personal control) are more elusive due to historical and environmental factors, such as a history of defeat, inadequacy and lack of control. Finally, persons with disabilities are embedded in a culture of loss. Important people routinely enter and exit their lives with very little warning. Ending the therapeutic relationship is likely to precipitate previous experiences of loss and, if not carefully worked through, can leave these individuals with a host of new problems (Hollins, 1995).

To summarize, there are a number of obstacles, which arise over the course of providing therapy to people with disabilities. They include: an involvement in multiple service delivery systems whose goals may conflict with those of psychotherapy; referrals made by service providers who may be naive regarding the nature of psychotherapy for people with disabilities; naivete of the person referred regarding the nature of psychotherapy and how to best use the service; an increased risk of boundary violations; skill acquisition is complicated by both learned helplessness and cognitive impediments to learning; a limitation of task accomplishment by historical and environmental factors; and a summons of complicated feelings of loss generated by the ever-changing caregivers who enter and exit their lives.

The goal of this chapter is to explore concrete strategies which proactively address these issues and to facilitate the person's progress in psychotherapy.

Preparation for Therapy: Establishing a Therapeutic Contract

For people with a dual diagnosis, the emphasis of treatment is often on the amelioration of behavioral difficulties and stabilization of psychiatric symptoms. For these individuals, the mental health professional can play a central role in helping the individual to strive towards personally valued goals. There are many service providers who will actively seek out the involvement of mental health professionals; and, when the communication is handled sensitively, it can be a great benefit to the individual. Strategies can be shared, insight can be gained into contextual issues, and new skills can be fostered in the natural environment. The natural environment consists of wherever the person lives, works or plays.

With most service providers, information is shared freely through vehicles such as case conferences and team meetings. Many are accustomed to knowing and taking into consideration all details of the individual's life when making treatment decisions. It is the norm for service providers to be intensely involved in aspects of persons with disabilities lives that most non-disabled individuals would experience as intrusive. Persons with disabilities experience their lives in full view of concerned others. Their toileting schedule, eating habits, choice in friends, socialization skills, use of leisure time, and sexual preferences are all fodder for clinical discussion. The violation of basic privacy is a reality for most people with disabilities. It is a part of their culture, and an evil that is often necessitated by responsibilities of oversight and protection (Levitas & Gilson, 1997). Unless the purpose of psychotherapy is clarified between the therapist and the person making the referral individual prior to the onset of treatment, it will be expected that the mental health professional join into well-established patterns of communication. Clarifying roles must go beyond explaining confidentiality in order for it to be accepted as an important aspect of the treatment environment. Failure to do so may result in the mental health professional being perceived as "withholding" as well as fostering an adversarial relationship between him/herself and other concerned parties.

What do service providers need to know about psychotherapy? Many are aware that psychotherapy can be helpful. Indeed, the person would not have been referred if that belief were not held. Most, unless they have had training in or direct experience with therapy, view the process as mysterious and may hold misconceptions about what transpires behind closed doors. A brief review of basic principles of psychotherapy, and what they as service providers can do to facilitate the process, can do much to avoid potential boundary violations and set the stage for supporting budding skills in the natural environment. Subjects which merit discussion include:

1) What is psychotherapy?

2) What is a therapeutic relationship?

3) What are some common ingredients of effective psychotherapy?

4) How is the support provider's relationship with the individual different from other helping relationships?

5) What kind of relationship will the therapist have with the referring service provider and other involved individuals?

6) How important is confidentiality, and what are the conditions which will necessitate breaking confidentiality?

7) How will communication be handled between the therapist and service provider?

It often is helpful to provide this information about psychotherapy in the form of a fact sheet that outlines important points. The advantage of written materials is that it provides a permanent product that can be referred to when conditions essential to effective treatment are threatened. Table 1 provides an example of a fact sheet:

Table 1. Sample Psychotherapy Fact Sheet

Information about Psychotherapy
for
Families and Service Providers

Thank you for making a referral for psychotherapy. Contrary to popular beliefs, psychotherapy is an effective treatment for people with disabilities in helping them to cope with everyday concerns and longstanding problems. Therapy works by helping the person look at his/her thoughts, feelings and behaviors in a supportive environment in order to help the person to develop better coping skills. There are several important aspects of psychotherapy that are essential in order for people to get the most benefit from the experience.

1. What is discussed during sessions must be kept private (confidential). Without privacy, the referred will have trouble trusting his/her therapist and will not work honestly in treatment. In order to ensue that confidentiality is maintained, communication must be handled sensitively. You can help protect privacy by adhering to the following guidelines:

   a) You must provide information to the therapist at any time. Information that is brought to the attention of the therapist will be discussed with the person in a manner that he/she can understand.

   b) Nothing discussed during therapy sessions will be released to you without the person's permission. When appropriate, the therapist will work with the person towards including you in various aspects of his/her treatment. The only exception to this is if the person is in danger of harming his/herself or someone else. Then the therapist will work directly with you to ensure the safety of all involved.

   c) If you require documentation for services rendered, the therapist will work with you to develop a system of documentation which protects the person's privacy.

2. Another important part of therapy is learning new skills. In order for new skills to make a difference, they must be practiced and supported in the natural environment. You are an important part of this process and may be asked to help out with making sure the person gets the most out of treatment. It takes patience when teaching new skills and sometimes things take longer or are more difficult while the person is learning.

3. The person must come to therapy consistently in order to get the most benefit. Please help make the person comes regularly and on time.

If you have comments or concerns regarding the person's treatment, please call the therapist to discuss them.

Preparing for Therapy: Teaching Prerequisite Skills

People with developmental disabilities enter into the process of psychotherapy with several disadvantages. Much like children or adolescents, they are usually referred for therapy by concerned others rather than establishing a therapeutic contact on their own accord. As a result, there is a great deal of confusion, anxiety, and ambiguity attached to the referral for psychotherapy. This may be especially true when prior contact with mental health professionals has been limited to evaluations of their disability (e.g., intelligence testing, special education placement). The ambiguity inherent in being referred for treatment, combined with cognitive limitations, leaves persons with developmental disabilities at a loss with respect to what to make of the therapeutic setting. They don't know why they are there, what they're supposed to do, and what the boundaries and benefits of participating in therapy are. Without setting a therapeutic agenda, they are often trapped in open-ended discussions of practical day to day concerns. Not only is this detrimental to the person being seen for treatment, but it is frustrating for both the treating and referring clinicians who are both aware that there are significant therapeutic issues to be addressed.

Providing individuals who have developmental disabilities with training and support can enhance their participation in and satisfaction with the services they receive. Although all service providers (both referring professionals and treating clinicians) can participate in educating the individual, the emphasis should be on helping the person make use of psychotherapy as independently as possible. An effective strategy for teaching people to use therapy services should address three issues: exploration of emotions surrounding entering treatment; education regarding the treatment process; and, environmental supports to facilitate independent participation in therapy.

The first step in preparing individuals for psychotherapy is to provide them with emotional support. Entering therapy arouses anxiety for most people, and this may be even more accentuated for people with disabilities. Because of prior negative experiences with mental health professionals, these individuals may need reassurance that they are not being sent to see a therapist as a punishment or to evaluate their disability. Emotional support must be given prior to introducing any new information, as anxiety surrounding the referral can interfere with the processing and retention of information that will help them learn how to use the service. Emotional support can be provided either by the treating therapist or a trusted caregiver in the person's natural environment.

Once persons with disabilities feel emotionally supported, they are more receptive to learning. They can then be taught:

a. What psychotherapy is (i.e., a place where they can talk about their thoughts and feelings, a place where people learn to solve their problems);
b. Why people go to therapy (i.e., private place to learn new things);
c. What happens in psychotherapy (i.e., talking, the boundaries of confidentiality, skill development and role playing);
d. What to talk about (i.e., all areas of life, good things, worries that do not go away, how they feel about themselves, and the importance of being honest).

Environmental supports may be needed to help the person incorporate what he/she has been taught and to plan what the individual would like to discuss during therapy sessions. A paper and pencil worksheet is one way to assist the individual with developing an agenda for scheduled therapy sessions. Any worksheet designed should be tailored to the individual's cognitive level and style of communication. Pictures are a helpful addition for individuals who have limited written skills or need visual cues in order to report abstract concepts such as feeling states. The worksheet can cover the following areas:

a. Home life, what they liked and what they wished was different.
b. Work life, what they liked and what they wished was different.

c. Interpersonal relationships, what they liked and what they wished was different.
d. Leisure time, what they liked and what they wished was different.
e. Any problems encountered during the week, how the problem was handled and personal satisfaction with how it was handled.
f. What made them happy, sad, angry, or worried over the past week?
g. How they felt about themselves that week.
h. What they would like help with that week.

Example: Psychotherapy Worksheet

Psychotherapy Worksheet

What happened at home this week?

☺What did you like?
☹What did you wish was different?

What happened with your boyfriend/girlfriend this week?
☺What did you like?
☹What did you wish was different?

What did you do for fun this week?
☺What did you like?
☹What did you wish was different?
Today I feel:

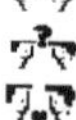

Angry Confused Happy

Today I would like help with:

Most people need assistance when environmental supports, such as worksheets, are first introduced. Prompting, modeling, and praise are all effective in enhancing learning. As the person becomes more familiar with the format, this assistance should fade out. Caregivers who are training the individual to use environmental supports should be cautioned against questioning the validity of what the person reports. They should be taught to only gently suggest that the person may want to bring an issue to the therapist's attention. Completed worksheets can be brought to therapy sessions and used as a guide for discussion.

Case Example#1

Ms. A is a 34-year-old woman with mild mental retardation and major depression. She currently lives in a community residence with nine other disabled adults and has a job within the community, employed on a part time basis. Shortly after Ms. A moved into her current residence, it became apparent that she had a number of emotional difficulties. Some could be attributed to adjustment issues (her father had died approximately one month prior to moving into her new home), while others appeared to be long standing. Most notable was Ms. A's extreme dependency upon her boyfriend, her willingness to accept abusive behavior on his part, and her need to carefully control her emotions and put on a happy face. Ms. A's residential provider referred her for psychotherapy to address the above issues. Over a four year period, Ms. A saw several therapists, none of whom were able to make any progress with desired goals or changing behavior. Ms. A became increasingly resistant to attending therapy, partly because the very thought of attending therapy undercut her already fragile coping skills. At the same time, her presenting problems intensified. She became paranoid, emotionally labile, and began to display both dangerous and self-abusive behaviors. Because of the severity of her difficulties, terminating treatment (albeit ineffective treatment) seemed inappropriate. Unfortunately, Ms. A's therapist no longer felt that therapy could continue and was considering discharging her to another professional's care. It was at this point that Ms. A began receiving support and education regarding her use of psychotherapy. Ms. A's response to this intervention produced a positive response. The most immediate benefit was a decrease in Ms. A's anxiety surrounding therapy. The process had been normalized and demystified for her and she was able to give herself permission to participate in the process. In addition, she began to explore substantive issues as opposed to day to day concerns.

Case Example#2

Mr. B is a 40-year-old man with Asperger's Syndrome. He currently lives in a community residence with nine other disabled adults and is competitively employed full time. He has been in therapy with the same therapist for over ten years. Mr. B has no major mental health issues, other than social difficulties associated with his developmental disability and his reasons for being involved in long term therapy were unclear. It appears that Mr. B continued in psychotherapy because his parents had set up the sessions, and he feared repercussions from either his therapist or parents if he decided to discontinue treatment. He was quite fearful of telling his therapist anything, believing that his therapist would react in a punitive fashion. After Mr. B began receiving support and education, he began to question the role the therapist played in his life (he viewed his therapist as a substitute parent) and began taking more control over the process.

Introducing New Skills: Empowering the Person to Make Therapeutic Change

Imagine that the following is your life. You are born developmentally disabled. Your parents argue about how to best take care of you. Your mother "babies" you, she's afraid that you will get hurt. Your father withdraws from you and is embarrassed that you're "not normal". Your younger siblings learn faster than you do, and before you know it they are doing things that you are not allowed to do. Your body is clumsy and slow and you have trouble remembering things. It is hard to make sense out of everything happening around you. You look different than other children. They tease you, and will not play with you. Nobody wants to be your friend. You learn pretty quickly that other people are smarter than you are, and nobody trusts you to make good decisions - even yourself. Sometimes you have seizures and lose control over your body, afterwards you feel funny and confused. You go to a special school where the people there are pretty strange. You have trouble communicating what you need. Sometimes, you freak out and lose control. You get sent to see special doctors to "fix" your problems. You do not get many opportunities to explore on your own - family and helpers are involved in all areas of your life (even the ones that you would rather keep private). Your family cannot deal with all of your special needs, so you go to live in a residential school with other people who have problems. You move into a group home. You do not have any choice about where you live or who you live with - you're told you are lucky. Sometimes the people that you live with have problems of their own - you do not know how to cope with them. You have a counselor that is there to help you. You like having a counselor, but each time you get used to one they leave. It is hard to trust people. You go to a workshop during the day + it is crowded and noisy. When there is work, you get paid only a small amount of money - when there is no work, you sit around and do nothing. You have a girlfriend/boyfriend. It is hard to get to see him/her. Other people decide what you can and cannot do together. How would you feel about yourself if this was your life experience? How would you view other people? How would you view the world around you?

Clearly, persons with disabilities face significant obstacles over the course of their life span. They are often ostracized, rejected, separated from natural supports as a child, only to enter into adulthood with little choice in major areas of their lives. In many cases, they live in environments which stress the coping skills that they possess, further reducing the likelihood that they will be successful (Levey & Howells, 1991). Social support, an important aspect of coping and preventing mental health disturbances is frequently lacking (Reiss & Benson, 1985; Benson, Reiss, Smith, & Laman, 1985). The focus of their lives, and the job of those that support them, is on habilitation-fixing deficits.

When the individual life histories of people with disabilities are reviewed and taken in the context of their current lives, it is not surprising that most hold strong beliefs regarding their ability to make changes. These beliefs, or cognitive distortions, grow out of common psychosocial experiences associated with having a developmental disability and include frequent failure, social isolation, and the stigmatizing features of having a disability (Reynolds & Miller, 1985; Reiss & Benson, 1982; Zigler & Hodapp, 1986).

Consider the impact of frequent failures. People with developmental disabilities, by the very nature of their problem, have greater difficulty in acquiring and using important skills of daily life. As a result, they experience failure at a higher rate and enter new situations with a low expectation of success. Reactions to chronic failure may include learned helplessness, dependence on others, and a negative self-image (Zigler & Hodapp, 1986).

The pervasiveness of learned helplessness in people with disabilities is well documented and the underlying beliefs that accompany these feelings are an impediment to making therapeutic change (Jones, Miller, Williams & Goldthorp, 1997). The individual who displays learned helplessness may appear passive and unable to see the value in attempting something new. Often this stems from a global belief that the person is powerless to influence events around them and they are "stuck" with whatever comes their way. In this case, the task of the therapist is to help the individual reframe events with an eye towards emphasizing the situations wherein the individual acts in a competent way and gains a sense of control over his/her own life.

Outer directed orientation is a term used to describe the person who is overly dependent upon others for functioning on a daily basis. This tendency to look to others as a guide for one's own behavior may be expressed in a more subtle fashion. Persons who adopt an outer directed stance have profound doubts about their own capabilities and view others as more competent. As a result, they may present themselves as overly dependent and cautious, or display contradictions in their decision making. For example, they may make decisions by following the cues of another as opposed to acting in a way that is in their own best interest. The tendency towards outer directedness can be exploited as a mechanism for shifting towards independent thought. The therapist can role model independent decision making as an indirect way of reducing outer directedness and encouraging self-direction.

It is well documented that social support is a critical factor in emotional well-being (Schloss, 1982). This holds true for people with disabilities as well. Unfortunately, rejection and isolation that epitomize our society's mores often characterize their experiences in life. This limits their opportunity to learn important skills, deprives them of important support, and creates distortions in how they view themselves and other people (Reiss & Benson, 1985).

Typically, persons with disabilities develop a view of themselves as unlikable and of other people as threatening. Behaviors which might be manifested include either a positive or negative reaction tendency (Zigler, Balla, & Butterfield, 1968). In the case of a positive reaction tendency, the person displays an overwhelming desire to please other people and "be liked". They appear to need continual positive feedback and emotional support from others. This stance interferes with the therapeutic process in a number of ways (Merighi, Edison, & Zigler, 1990). These persons may be reluctant to discuss problems and will adjust their behavior in session to what they believe will most likely be received as positive. In the case of a negative reaction tendency those with disabilities display an overwhelming desire to avoid potentially painful rejections. They devalue the situation (make something potentially good into something undesirable) so that potential negative feelings can be avoided. They are reluctant to form relationships and therefore may behave in either a passive, withdrawn manner or in a hostile way. Individuals with this orientation are at high risk for leaving therapy prematurely due to inherent difficulties in developing and participating in a therapeutic relationship.

People with disabilities are often painfully aware of their value in society. From a very early age, they see that there is high value in appearing "normal" and very little value in being disabled (Reiss & Benson, 1982). It is hard to develop a positive sense of self under these circumstances. As a result, many people with disabilities have a very negative view of themselves and low self-esteem. They operate on the belief that being disabled is bad and "normal" is good. This belief may reveal itself any number of ways over the course of treatment. These individuals may deny any evidence of their disability, either directly or by avoiding situations wherein their limitation may become evident. They may also display a hatred for all others with disabilities, refusing to socialize with other disabled individuals, and referring to themselves as "higher functioning". They may also see themselves as inherently damaged, incompetent, and unlovable.

Beliefs related to being disabled are very similar to those posed by Beck in his cognitive theory of depression (Beck, Rush, Shaw, & Emery, 1979). He notes that people who are depressed display the following cognitive triad: having a negative view of the self (seeing oneself in negative terms such as ugly, unlovable or "bad"); having a negative view of the world (perceiving the world in negative terms such as hostile, scary and punishing); and, having a negative view of the future (viewing the future in negative terms like hopeless, bad outcomes).

An important part of restoring a person's sense of self-control involves having him/her reframe distressing events or behaviors as signs of coping. Meichenbaum (1994) describes several effective strategies for reframing beliefs that are easily applied to people with disabilities (p. 414). He advocates the use of several lines of questioning to accomplish this task, including:

1) Asking evidence based questions: Does the data match the person's belief?
2) Asking alternative based questions: Are there other ways to explain events?
3) Asking implication based questions: Does the data mean everything the person thinks it means?

Asking evidence-based questions involves having the person examine how well underlying beliefs match reality. For example, a common cognitive distortion involves the person maintaining the belief that he/she is inherently unlovable. Having the person compare the belief with evidence to the contrary challenges this belief. Most beliefs are extreme and do not hold up to objective examination. Alternative based questions ask the person to generate other possible explanations for events around them. Typically, these people misattribute the behavior and intentions of others as having more to do with them than is actually the case. For people with disabilities, this may even have a developmental component (frequently children believe their thoughts and actions have a greater impact on environmental events than is true). When events are critically examined, many alternative explanations can be generated. Asking implication based questions involve having the person determine if the conclusions he/she is drawing from information in the environment is valid, and using similar experimental strategies.

Case Example #1

Mr. A. is a 30-year-old man with autism who was referred for therapy due to verbally aggressive and self-injurious behavior. He entered therapy with profound feelings of helplessness. Mr. A believed that many of his problems were due to being "inappropriately placed" (he has never lived with a group of individuals with similar disabilities), "misdiagnosed" (he spent his childhood bouncing between mental health and mental retardation facilities), or because the problems associated with his disability precluded him from having a satisfying life. He suffered sexual abuse as a young man while living in residential schools. He often described himself as "a weakling, not a man at all, unable to defend myself". Just prior to beginning psychotherapy, Mr. A failed in an apartment program, was briefly institutionalized, and then moved into a group home for individuals with disabilities. Shortly after moving into his group home, Mr. A decompensated and was hospitalized psychiatrically twice in a period of six months.

Mr. A had many reasons for feeling hopeless and helpless. The focus of his entire life had been on his disabilities and the multitude of problems that accompanied them. Yet in spite of his difficulties, he maintained an excellent sense of humor. He enjoyed word games and used them as a vehicle for expressing his feelings. He was driven by a desire to improve himself. Periodically, he would rally the motivation to try things that had resulted in failure in the past. The process of empowerment began by helping him to see that he was able to cope with extraordinarily difficult circumstances in spite of his disability.

For Mr. A, it was important for him to discover for himself that at the heart of these successes were the seeds of very important coping skills and the basis for making change in his life. Simply pointing out and reinforcing coping skills would have been perceived as infantalizing. Mr. A was presented with gentle questions such as "how is it that you keep your sense of humor in spite of spending the last 2 months in the hospital," or "how did you manage to survive all those kids picking on you?" These questions were excellent strategies for helping him reframe his experience. These types of questions were effective because they seemed to simultaneously empathize with difficult circumstances while pointing out how he managed to cope. After Mr. A was able to see how he had coped in the past, his willingness to expand his repertoire of coping skills increased.

Case Example #2

Mr. C is a man with mild mental retardation who was referred for psychotherapy to address verbally aggressive outbursts and work refusal. During the initial phase of therapy, it quickly became clear that he suffered from both pervasive paranoid ideation and feelings of depression. Mr. C was locked in a cycle of cognitive distortions which perpetuated his sense of isolation, loneliness, and depression. He believed that others stared at him with the intention of harming him and his only recourse for self-protection was to lash out verbally at others. Others in turn either avoided Mr. C or responded to him with aggression. There was a historical basis in reality to these beliefs, as Mr. C had spent most of his life living in institutions where there was a high incidence of violence and aggression. Fortunately, Mr. C was now living in a group home were his daily circumstances were less threatening. Mr. C was first helped to see that someone might look at him for a variety of reasons - maybe he looked familiar to them, or maybe they wanted to get to know him better. This led to Mr. C experimenting with new ways of responding to people (for example, smiling and saying hello) as a means of finding out why others looked at him. Direct experience with society at large began to teach him that not everyone was interested in harming him.

Introducing New Skills: Ensuring that Skills are Supported in the Natural Environment

By definition, people with developmental disabilities have cognitive limitations and difficulty learning new material. In order for even the simplest of skills to be learned, they must be practiced on a regular basis. Opportunity to practice new skills cannot be limited to the therapy session. In one study of social skills training (Senatore, Matson, & Kazdin, 1982), the authors found that although people who received social skills training performed better than those who did not, individuals who engaged in active rehearsal in the natural environment displayed greater generalization and maintenance of skills six months after the termination of treatment.

Facilitating opportunities to practice and use new skills outside the therapy session requires the cooperation of those supporting individuals in their natural environment. This must be handled sensitively in order to preserve the integrity of the therapeutic relationship. First and foremost, the individual must be involved in the decision to share what he/she is learning in therapy with those that are involved in other aspects of his/her life.

When helping individuals recognize the importance of carrying over skills into the natural environment, the therapist must take into account how the new skills will be received by significant others in their daily life. Some new skills will be welcomed by the significant others, such as when a person begins to display improved impulse control or new, more appropriate social skills. With minimal resistance, the skills are likely to be welcomed and reinforced in the natural environment. Other skills, such as assertiveness, may produce mixed results. For example, in situations where compliance with rules is important, budding assertion may result in new problems, such as social conflict or increased suppression of the person's thoughts and feelings. All consequences of changing behavior should be thoroughly explored.

Once the person has agreed to include others in his/her treatment, the task of helping the person enlist outside support begins. This is best handled as a collaborative process, with the person and the therapist working together to help concerned individuals understand how they can be of help. Important information to communicate includes a thorough rationale for the new skill - how it will ultimately be helpful to the individual; situations where the new skill can be encouraged; strategies for encouraging the new skill; and, strategies for reinforcing the new skill.

If prompting, corrective feedback or reinforcement are necessary components of teaching the new skill, it is helpful for the therapist to demonstrate how to properly facilitate practice sessions. This allows the involved caregiver to see how the skills should be taught, rather than relying on his/her own interpretation of the therapist's instruction. In order to ensure that they understand how to facilitate practice sessions, time should also be devoted to observing caregivers implement therapeutic procedures.

Case Example

Ms. B is a woman in her 40's with diagnoses of both mild mental retardation and histrionic personality disorder. She spent the preponderance of her life institutionalized in state psychiatric hospitals, but has been successful at remaining in a community-based placement for the past two years. Ms. B was referred for psychotherapy to address verbally and physically aggressive behavior. At the onset of treatment, Ms. B was described as provocative, and she engaged in frequent conflicts with both staff and peers. The police were periodically called to her group home when her behavior was out of control. Over the course of treatment, therapy addressed several issues including improving her self-esteem, nurturing prosocial behaviors addressing an underlying hostility bias, increasing personal control, and developing problem solving skills. In order for these skills to be fostered in the natural environment, a good deal of cooperation needed to take place between the therapist and primary care providers. With Ms. B's permission, important people in her natural environment were invited to attend scheduled therapy sessions. During those sessions, Ms. B was assisted in explaining what she was learning and how she could be helped to practice these skills.

Inviting concerned others into the therapy session had several advantages. It respected the integrity of the therapeutic relationship and avoided talking about Ms. B outside her presence. This was critical in Ms. B's treatment, as her cognition often had a paranoid flavor, and under ambiguous circumstances she would interpret events negatively. Secondly, it allowed the therapist to demonstrate teaching strategies and observe how direct care staff would implement strategies. It often took multiple trials to ensure that direct care staff understood and could implement training strategies correctly. And if the contact had been limited to telephone consultation or mere explanation of the skills being trained, interventions would not have been carried over as effectively. Finally, because of the integration of concerned others into the therapeutic setting, learnable skills were formally integrated into Ms. B's overall habilitative programming.

Ending Psychotherapy

Careful attention must be paid to how therapy ends in order to ensure that therapeutic gains are maintained and the likelihood of relapse is minimized. Meichenbaum (1994) outlines four tasks to accomplish during the termination phase of therapy. They are: (a) To bolster self-confidence, sense of competency and self-efficacy, (b) to discuss future goals and strategies for coping, (c) to discuss relapse prevention, and (d) to arrange for booster sessions (p. 335).

The same goals hold true when working with people with disabilities. Accomplishing these goals tend to be somewhat more complicated due to life experiences associated with having a disability, including: (a) The chronic challenges associated with having a disability, (b) less opportunity for, and experience with, independent activity, (c) a tendency to form dependent relationships on helpers, and (d) a context of loss is embedded in their lives.

When treating the individual with developmental disabilities, it is important to acknowledge the chronic nature of challenges associated with having a developmental disability. No amount of psychotherapy will change cognitive limitations. It is also likely that psychosocial stressors that contribute to emotional difficulties will persist beyond termination. If treatment has been successful, the goal should be for the individual to cope as adaptively as possible with life's challenges. For some individuals, this will lead to a deeper exploration of issues related to their disability and its resolution allows for greater comfort with life circumstances. The need for ongoing assistance should be acknowledged and the individual can be helped in developing a network of supports.

There are many reasons why people with disabilities have less experience with independent activity. As children, they may have been overprotected and given limited opportunity to take risks. As adults, they are often living in situations where successful adaptation requires a certain degree of dependence and loss of autonomy. Activities such as dinnertime, self-care tasks, and leisure may fall outside of the individual's control. As a result, the person may fall into the habit of waiting to be told what to do. When the person with developmental disabilities attempts independent action, he/she may be labeled "noncompliant" and be subjected to behavioral interventions which foster and reinforce adherence to group living rules. The prospect of assuming more responsibility and acting independently represents a significant departure from well-established rules of living. As with fostering new skills, restoring a person's autonomy and sense of self control requires the cooperation of people intimately involved in the individual's day to day life. This may involve teaching the caregiver the importance of self-direction and how to increase the individual's opportunity for control over important events.

The tendency for people with disabilities to form dependent relationships and issues of ongoing loss are interrelated. People with disabilities often identify with and prefer to associate with staff members. Much of this stems from the discomfort in associating with other people who have disabilities and their perceived undesirability. Being with other people with disabilities often reminds them of their own shortcomings; a fact that is often painfully avoided (Szivos & Griffiths, 1990). Associating exclusively with staff members decreases the person's social network and increases dependency on supports that exist. Direct service workers often develop the closest relationships with people with disabilities. Unfortunately, the average direct care worker leaves approximately every eight months. This can leave the person in a chronic state of loss and more dependant on remaining interpersonal contacts. As therapy prepares to end, achievements are tempered by feelings of loss - the loss of the therapist, of special time, of a special relationship. It is not uncommon for current losses to trigger previous ones. In many cases, this is a result of previous mishandling of other experiences. This is particularly true around issues such as death and dying and it is common to hear that a person with disabilities fails to participate in normal rituals of bereavement (i.e., funeral attendance) for their own "protection" (Hollins, 1995).

People with disabilities attempt to avoid and cope with loss in a variety of ways. Sometimes the person acts indifferent to loss - it can't hurt if it wasn't important. People who have trouble verbalizing their feelings may display disruptive behaviors. Others might perseverate on previous losses, displaying feelings that may seem out of proportion with current circumstances. Similar to children, who often believe that their actions are responsible for a person's departure, people with disabilities may feel responsible for the loss. In some cases, they may have a history of displaying maladaptive behavior which may in fact contribute to a staff member leaving. Other people display regression in an attempt to reengage the helper, behaviorally communicating "how can you leave me now when I need you most?"

Addressing loss proactively can minimize some of the above reactions. How the loss is processed is dictated to some degree by the circumstances under which therapy is ending. When therapy ends as a result of goal attainment, completing one's treatment can be cause for celebration. Special activities or shared tasks can help to bring a positive experience to closure. For example, a dinner out, graduation ceremony, or other symbolic act can help these individuals consolidate skills and experience a sense of accomplishment. When therapy ends under less favorable circumstances (for example, the individual is pulled out of treatment), the individual must be given the opportunity to discuss reasons for termination, and given reassurance regarding their ability to cope with difficult circumstances and receive the help they need. In either situation, it is important to invite a discussion of their feelings associated with ending psychotherapy. Given previous experiences with loss, these individuals may be reluctant to discuss those feelings and often must be invited and encouraged to explore these issues. When discussing loss, careful attention should be paid to how it was handled in the past and the person with a disability should be given ample opportunity to ask questions and receive emotional support. In the absence of historical closure, the therapist can create new opportunities.

Gradual termination is preferable to an abrupt ending of therapy sessions. Gradually reducing the frequency of therapy sessions enables the person to become accustomed to seeing the therapist less often. At this time, it is also a good idea to work on building natural supports in the person's environment and transferring the role of trusted confidante to someone to whom the individual has access to a regular basis. This may involve helping the individual to develop the necessary social skills needed to be involved in an intimate relationship. It may also involve having these individuals broaden their social network so that there are many individuals in their lives who can provide them with the social support needed to buffer the effects of future stressors.

Meichenbaum (1994) stated that individuals should leave therapy with the belief that their goal is to cope the best that they can, rather than master every situation they encounter. They should be taught to "anticipate, accept, and cope with possible lapses, setbacks and re-experiences", particularly when under stress (p. 335). Involved caretakers should also be familiar with this concept and be prepared to provide these individuals with additional support, including having an avenue for reestablishing their relationship with the therapist should the need arise. The therapist can proactively schedule quarterly "check ups" in order to provide the individual with a sense of continuity; moreover, the therapist can intervene early should circumstances warrant further support.

Summary

The process of providing psychotherapy to individuals with disabilities is complicated, given both individual and contextual factors. Obstacles arise over the course of therapy that must be proactively addressed in order to ensure that the person benefits from what transpires during the therapy hour. The following represents a checklist of items which the therapist can address in order to ensure that each issue is handled both sensitively and appropriately:

1. Spend time educating service providers regarding the nature of psychotherapy.
2. Clarify roles, boundaries, and methods of communication prior to beginning a therapeutic relationship with a person who is disabled.
3. Educate the individual regarding the nature of psychotherapy. Address fears, misconceptions, and give a framework for generating his/her own therapeutic agenda.
4. Empower the individual to begin to make changes in his/her life. Directly address cognitive distortions, particularly those surrounding sense of self-efficacy.
5. Ensure that outside providers will support new skills being learned in psychotherapy. Educate service providers regarding the rationale for learning the new skills as well as providing them with concrete strategies for prompting and reinforcing these skills.
6. Plan for terminating the therapeutic relationship. Use it as an opportunity for exploring past losses and bringing the client to closure. Teach the person to believe that future problems are likely, and that he/she has the skills needed to handle those situations.
7. Fade out therapy sessions. Schedule quarterly (or semiannual) "check ups".
8. Be prepared to reenter the person's life should the need arise.

References

Beck, A.T., Rush, A.J., Shaw, B.F., & Emery, G. (1979). *Cognitive therapy of depression.* New York : Guilford Press.

Benson, B.A., Reiss, S., Smith, D.C., & Laman, D.S. (1985). Psychosocial correlates of depression in mentally retarded adults: II. Poor social skills. *American Journal of Mental Deficiency, 89*, 657-659.

Carr, E.G, Levin, L., McConnachie, G., Carlson, J.I., Kemp, D.C., & Smith, C.E. (1994). *Communication-based intervention for problem behavior: A user's guide for producing positive change.* Baltimore: Paul H. Brookes.

Hollins, S. (1995). Managing grief better: People with developmental disabilities. *The Habilitative Mental Healthcare Newsletter*, *14*, 50-52.

Jones, R.B.P., Miller, B., Williams, H., & Goldthorp, J. (1997). Theoretical and practical issues in cognitive-behavioral approaches for people with learning disabilities: A radical behavioral approach. In Kroese, Dagnan, & Loumidis (Eds.), *Cognitive-behavior therapy for people with learning disabilities.* New York: Routledge.

Kroese, B.S. (1997). Cognitive-behavior therapy for people with learning disabilities: Conceptual and contextual issues. In Kroese, Dagnan, & Loumidis (Eds.), *Cognitive-behavior therapy for people with learning disabilities.* New York: Routledge.

Levey, S., & Howells, K. (1991). Anger and its management. *Journal of Forensic Psychiatry*, *1,* 305-327.

Levitas, A., & Gilson, S.F. (1997). Individual psychotherapy for persons with mild and moderate mental retardation. *NADD Newsletter*, *13*, 4. Kingston NY: NADD Press.

Matson, J.L., & Gardner, W.I. (1991). Behavioral learning theory and current application to severe behavior problems in persons with mental retardation. *Clinical Psychology Review*, *11*, 175-183.

Meichenbaum, D. (1994). *A clinical handbook/practical therapist manual for assessing and treating adults with post-traumatic stress disorder (PTSD).* Waterloo, Canada: Institute Press.

Merighi, J., Edison, M., & Zigler, E. (1990). The role of motivational factors in the functioning of mentally retarded individuals. In R. M. Hodapp, J.A. Burack, & E. Zigler (Eds.), *Issues in the developmental approach to mental retardation*. Cambridge: Cambridge University Press.

Reiss, S., & Benson, B. (1985). Psychosocial correlates of depression in mentally retarded adults: I. Minimal social support and stigmatization. *American Journal of Mental Deficiency*, *89*, 331-337.

Reiss, S., & Benson, B. (1982). Awareness of negative social conditions among mentally retarded, emotionally disturbed outpatients. *American Journal of Psychiatry*, *141*, 88-90.

Reynolds, W.M., & Miller, K.L. (1985). Depression and learned helplessness in mentally retarded and non-mentally retarded adolescents: An initial investigation. *Applied Research in Mental Retardation*, *6*, 295-306.

Roback, H.B., & Shelton, M. (1995). Effects of confidentiality limitations on the psychotherapeutic process. *Journal of Psychotherapy Research and Practice*, *3,* 185-193.

Schloss, P.J. (1982). Verbal interaction patterns in depressed and non-depressed institutionalized mentally retarded adults. *Applied Research in Mental Retardation*, *3,* 1-12.

Senatore, V., Matson, J.L., & Kazdin, A. E. (1982). A comparison of behavioral methods to train social skills to mentally retarded adults. *Behavior Therapy*, *13*, 313-324.

Szivos, S.E., & Griffiths, E. (1990). Group processes involved in coming to terms with a mentally retarded identity. *Mental Retardation*, *28*, 331-341.

Szymanski, L.S., & Rosefsky, Q.B. (1980). *Group psychotherapy with retarded persons: Assessment, treatment, and consultation* (pp.173-194). Baltimore: University Park Press.

Zigler, E., & Hodapp, R. M. (1986). *Understanding mental retardation.* Cambridge: University Press.

Zigler, E., Balla, D., & Butterfield, E.C. (1968). A longitudinal investigation of the relationship between preinstitutional social deprivation and social motivation in institutionalized retardates. *Journal of Personality and Social Psychology, 10*, 437-445.

CHAPTER THREE

TRANSFERENCE/COUNTERTRANSFERENCE IN INDIVIDUAL PSYCHOTHERAPY

Andrew Levitas, M.D. and Stephen Gilson, Ph.D.

Resolution of the transference relationship is considered to be the heart of the process of psychodynamic psychotherapy, so much so that Rogers and Dyamond (1954) dismissed the possibility of psychodynamic psychotherapy for individuals with mental retardation because of assumed failure of insight due to impairments in verbal communication and other intellectual capabilities and, because ". . .self-reliance is intrinsic in psychotherapy, and this trait is often absent in the mentally retarded".

Persons with mental retardation think concretely; that is, unlike the adult who is capable of abstract thinking, the person with mental retardation uses information-processing strategies based almost exclusively upon sophisticated manipulation of visible and tangible reality. For psychotherapeutic purposes, this mode of thinking demands reliance upon visual demonstrations, actions, and actuality rather than metaphor and memory. Various nonverbal methods of communication in therapy are proposed: gestures (Ruesch & Kees, 1956); figure drawing (Sternlicht, 1966); and play and concrete activity, for example, going out into the community (Szymanski, 1980). Szymanski also noted that, "Patients should be encouraged and taught to express (appropriately) opinions, ideas, feelings, and wishes." All of these techniques, and the resulting activity demanded of the therapist, are familiar from the child psychotherapy model, which can form the basis for an approach to psychodynamic psychotherapy with persons with mental retardation of all ages.

Rogers and Dyamond's second objection, the absence of self-reliance in individuals with mental retardation, and therefore, presumably, the inability to resolve dependency issues in the transference, has been only partially addressed. Beck (1962) stressed the importance of contact with parents. Sternlicht (1965) points to the dependence of the retarded patient upon institutional personnel and other professionals. Lott (1970) suggests that, "perhaps the first step in the program of psychotherapy with a disturbed retardate should start by counseling those upon whom he is dependent for care." Szymanski (1980) refers to this as "casework," a matter for routine therapeutic contact with caregivers.

Persons with mental retardation do have much in common with other dependent populations. Because of prejudice, upbringing, or the dynamics of support agencies, many people with mental retardation live in a way analogous to children: within a persistent web of relationships in which their ability to change their perceptions and behavior is limited by the capacity of their caregivers (families, counselors, case managers, supervisors, or employers) to share or respond to such changes. The child psychotherapist routinely meets with the patient's family and with personnel of agencies involved with the child patient. Problems leading to referral frequently reflect the imperatives and values of the systems with which the patient and his family are interacting, rather than the patient's or family's own needs and feelings. In many cases, the system's functioning may actually perpetuate the problem behavior. Inevitably, these powerful forces in the child's life become part of the therapeutic process; so caregivers must become part of the psychotherapy of a person with mental retardation. If the issue of dependency is addressed only with the caregiver, there remains the problems created for the patient by these "solutions."

That the traditional adult psychotherapy model must be modified in these ways to accommodate the needs of persons with mild and moderate mental retardation is undeniable, with resulting changes in the way communication takes place and a working relationship is built. For persons with severe and profound mental retardation transference and countertransference become the mode of communication and understanding. These modifications inevitably affect the ways in which transference and termination issues must be resolved, and create unusual countertransference issues (Levitas & Gilson, 1989). The following discussion of these issues assumes the reader's familiarity with the phenomena of transference and countertransference in psychodynamic psychotherapy. It begins with consideration of these phenomena in patients with mild and moderate mental retardation and concludes with a section on work with persons with severe and profound mental retardation.

The Subculture of Mental Retardation and Its Developmental Manifestations

Aman (1991) has noted that persons with mental retardation constitute a subculture. This subculture is set apart, even though its members grow up in "mainstream" homes and families, by a different developmental "track," with a different developmental endpoint than that observed in the "mainstream" culture, and a parallel but separate set of educational and habilitative institutions from that used by members of the "mainstream" culture. The different developmental track is characterized by a tendency to allow emotional experience and interchange to be mediated by others: a Mediated Self capable of briefly and reversibly incorporating some of the cognitive functioning of others into the self at times of stress (Levitas & Gilson, 1990, 1994) This personality structure leaves persons with mental retardation relatively more vulnerable to demands for increased autonomous functioning; persons with mental retardation who request psychotherapy or whose families seek psychotherapy for them most often are struggling with some life crisis or an impending life change.

Successful psychotherapy therefore involves not only understanding and resolving a particular neurotic conflict, but the issue and mechanisms of dependency in the life of the person in general. The transference is the encounter of the Mediated Self with an Other who is determined to minimize its need for mediation. On the model of Freud's famous aphorism about turning neurotic suffering into ordinary human misery, the task of the therapist working with the patient with mental retardation is to help turn neurotic clinging into ordinary human dependency.

Countertransference to Mental Retardation Itself

Before considering the countertransference to the individual patient, we must consider the countertransference to the phenomenon of mental retardation itself. This experience, rooted in the therapist's unconscious feelings about developmental disability, will operate to a greater or lesser extent with any patient with a developmental disability, even before the working relationship can begin. In a study of the perceptions of professions about individuals with disabilities by Gilson, Bricout and Baskind (in press), disabled participants noted that the preconceptions that social workers have about disability interfered with their ability to identify important distinctions within types of disabilities. Further, the participants reported that social workers commonly prejudge individuals on the basis of a disability label and/or severity of the visible disability; fail to recognize the uniqueness within the individual; establish instant one-way familiarity with the disabled person; resist the idea that the individual with the disability has many capabilities; and fail to seek the expert advice of the disabled persons themselves (Gilson et al., (in press). These findings may be characterized as social distancing, or what Hahn (1993) has more poignantly described as aesthetic anxiety and existential anxiety. Hahn (1993) suggests that aesthetic anxiety is experienced by the nondisabled person in response to the fears engendered by persons whose appearance deviates markedly from the usual or includes physical traits regarded as unappealing and existential anxiety is defined as the perceived threat that a disability could interfere with functional capabilities deemed necessary to the pursuit of a satisfactory life (p. 39).

The consequence of these feelings and beliefs, conscious and unconscious, for the individual with a developmental disability is that the clinician will enter the professional relationship with a preconceived set of beliefs about the individual based solely on the professional's perception of disability. That many of these preconceptions are erroneous has been ably demonstrated elsewhere (Asch & Fine, 1988; Wehman, Gilson, & Tusler, 1997; Zola, 1993). What is important for the discussion here is a recognition that these unconscious feelings and beliefs, countertransference to mental retardation itself, can have a serious impact upon the therapeutic relationship. As such, this aspect of countertransference must be identified and considered during each phase of the psychotherapeutic process.

Formation of the Working Relationship

Transference, the "transfer" of emotions and ways of relating from their original objects to the person of the therapist, operates from the first moments of contact. The patient has come for (or has been brought for) help, and therefore feels dependent to the degree he or she is accustomed to feel in any helping relationship. For persons with mental retardation, accustomed to be taught and helped at every turn, this means the operation of the Mediated Self, and they rely upon the therapist for answers, even for permission to express emotion. The first step in assessment and in building a working relationship is the establishment of communication with an individual whose capacity for formal and abstract thought may be limited, bearing in mind that these measures will inevitably affect the transference. Communication may have to be in concrete terms, and, without either overestimating or underestimating the patient's abilities, ways of asking permission to check the patient's degree of understanding must be negotiated. This can be as simple as asking, "Do people ever have a hard time understanding you, or do you ever have a hard time understanding them? Will you stop me if you do not understand me?" We must remember that these are questions which have their place in psychotherapy regardless of cognitive deficit. One must establish from the first that the cognitive deficit is a legitimate and neutral topic for discussion and assessment - a fact about the patient's life, and that the patient is expected to be an active partner in helping to adapt the therapeutic process to the need.

The next task is to deepen the relationship by the gathering of as complete and detailed a clinical and personal-developmental history as can possibly be managed. All sources of history should be explored: surviving family members, old medical charts, old social histories, family photographs, past psychological test reports and school records, and so on. The advantages are several fold. First, knowing the facts helps establish the dialogue with the patient - the more details one knows, the less often one has to ask the patient to stop during his associations and explain the context of his remarks. Second, other details may emerge, perhaps concerning conditions that were overlooked in previous evaluations, or conditions for which diagnostic criteria have been updated or expanded. A history consistent with pervasive developmental disorders, biochemical disorders, newly understood chromosome disorders, mood disorder, seizure or dyscontrol disorders can be found in the sometimes accidentally recorded details of an institutional record. Third, knowledge of the patient's cognitive abilities minimizes attribution of meaning to simple misunderstandings. Finally, and not of least importance, is that the history-taking process forms an alliance between the therapist and the other important people in the patient's life, as well as with the patient, who should be as active a partner in the process as circumstances permit (Levitas & Gilson, 1989).

This approach requires the informed consent of the patient (Szymanski, 1980). To say to a patient, "It sounds like many people make decisions in your life; I can best help you if I get to know them, too," is an empathic as well as a practical communication. Patients can and must be assured that these meetings will not compromise confidentiality. The best place for these meetings is the group home or school (so long as this does not cause the patient discomfort), since this will allow contact with the person's entire world - not just a primary counselor, but aides, secretaries, janitors, and so on, all of whom may play surprising and unexpectedly important roles, and it allows the therapist the opportunity to assess which are patient problems and which are system problems. The opportunity to form one's own impression of these people is priceless; one can later help the patient test his or her perceptions, and one may recognize these people in the transference. For the individual living more independently and working in a supported employment or competitive setting, sessions held in the therapist's office are the most appropriate.

Deepening of the Therapeutic Alliance: Consequences for the Transference

Transference is the term for interaction with the therapist based on the transfer of feelings from past relationships; countertransference is the therapist's corresponding interactions based on feelings from the therapist's past relationships. Corresponding terms for the patient's response to real and present aspects of the therapist and the relationship, and the therapist's response to real and present aspects of the patient and relationship are reaction and counter-reaction. The two orders of experience are connected; reaction and counter-reaction can affect transference and countertransference. The point is not to minimize reaction and counter-reaction, transference and countertransference, but to recognize them, understand their sources, and interpret them for the patient in ways that promote understanding and growth.

Szymanski (1980) supplies numerous examples of the necessity for deepening the therapeutic alliance through active "education" of the patient to the process of psychotherapy. He notes the fear of criticism, "based upon traumatic past experiences," and "dependency on the therapist and need for his approval." Rather, the fear of criticism and dependency is rooted in the patient's entire developmental experience (Levitas & Gilson, 1989, 1990, 1994). This reaction must be clarified early with acknowledgment of the accuracy of the patient's perception of the necessarily judgmental nature of evaluations of cognitive and functional deficits, and reminder and reassurance that psychotherapy is not a test, and that there are really, no "correct" answers, and there is no possibility of making a mistake as long as all remains in the realm of words.

One consequence of the Mediated Self is that people with mental retardation tend to experience all people without mental retardation as caregivers. Psychotherapists may be the latest of a long line of different kinds of therapists who will "fix" them, and do so without, or with little, volition or involvement on their part. This resembles the idealizing transference seen in patients with Borderline Personality Disorder, but in fact it more closely approximates the kinds of expectations children have of psychotherapists. Also as with children (who through early adolescence also rely on concrete thinking), the therapist's interpretations carry an aura of authority because they may be experienced as mind reading. These reactions must be confronted early and often. The only way to do this is to talk about mental retardation, and to talk frankly about the disparities between the lives of persons with mental retardation and the life of the therapist when the topic arises. The opportunity to do this occurs when the patient begins to ask the therapist for details about the therapist's life.

Persons with mental retardation ask many personal questions. This bears an unfortunate resemblance to the behavior of patients with severe personality disorders and schizophrenia, and therapists who prize therapeutic distance are in danger of responding as if to a patient incapable of appreciating ego boundaries. The patient's intrusiveness does not necessarily have pathological roots. It must be remembered that persons with mental retardation are permitted, and even subtly encouraged, to continue to interact with others (particularly caregivers) in ways characteristic of early stages of development. Many have scant opportunity to develop the sophistication required to understand the psychotherapeutic relationship at first. The patient will attempt to establish a relationship in the way he has learned to do - by asking about the other person. It can also be difficult for the person with mental retardation to find something to share that is in common with the therapist's world. It should also be remembered that persons with mental retardation (and their families) are routinely questioned by all sorts of professionals and paraprofessionals about the most minute details of their lives. The patient will inevitably ask about basics: Do you have a family? Do you have children? When are their birthdays? Do they go to school? Do you have any pets? Do you have a car or a truck? These are also concrete ways of finding out if the therapist is an experienced caregiver, analogous to another patient's examination of the therapist's credentials. It is a normal part of adolescence to develop the capacity to have a private life and to keep secrets. This is an aspect of development persons with mental retardation seldom get to experience; only adolescents who move into a peer culture develop the capacity to have secrets from caregivers, and this is what persons with mental retardation seldom have the opportunity to do (Levitas & Gilson, 1990, 1994).

Thus, the assumed simplicity of the patient's emotional life is perpetuated by the conditions of his development, and his style of establishing a relationship is at risk for being experienced by the therapist as primitive, seriously disturbed, or annoyingly intrusive. Recognizing the sources of this style of relating, the therapist should be prepared to answer these questions as openly and honestly as possible, and reply with questions about the patient's life. Less obvious equalities in the lives of the patient and therapist then emerge. It is possible to have in common with the patient an interest in music, in sports, in sex; to share with a person with mental retardation a knowledge of the pressures of economic hardship, the limited joys of public transportation and fast-food, and not least, the frustrations of life with parents and other powerful authorities. These experiences are common to us all and conversation about them - not just listening, or reflecting - provides the patient with the first of what can become a series of experiences of equality and independence. Szymanski (1980) says: " . . . the therapist must be (and feel comfortable in this role) a "real" person and not only a neutral therapeutic mirror." Persons with mental retardation may not respond to the abstract processes of listening or reflecting. To say to someone who uses concrete thinking, "I know how you must feel," may be meaningless without a concrete example from the therapist's life or experience. Szymanski (1980) notes that his also provides "direct role modeling." When one has established the verbal sharing process it is possible, and necessary, to explain concretely the process of psychotherapy (for example: "As we talk, we can begin to find out what's behind the things you do.") as a joint project of patient and therapist.

The need for interchange continues beyond such an explanation. The emotional reactions of persons with mental retardation are frequently limited by the responses of the people upon whom they depend. This may begin in families where patients are not allowed to grieve about their condition; their expressions of sadness or anger may be denied, or may be redirected into fruitless attempts to escape their conditions by studying harder. It is hard for a child to cry when his parents begin to cry, too. The emotional reaction that is thought to interfere with academic progress may be perceived as the problem rather than as the sign of a problem: rather than explore the sources of the child's reaction, behavioral programming may be used by professionals simply to stop it. In adolescence, the injunction against tears as being age-inappropriate may block the expression of sadness at all the losses of the patient's adolescence (Levitas & Gilson, 1989). Szymanski (1980) refers to this as a need to encourage and teach the person with mental retardation " . . . to express (appropriately) opinions, ideas, feelings and wishes." It is striking how few persons with mental retardation over the age of eighteen are known to cry, even in appropriate circumstances. That they do so in later stages of psychotherapy suggests that a limited emotional range is not a phenomenon intrinsic to mental retardation. Rather, this seems analogous to the plight of the child with a terminal illness, who is taken on endless trips to Disneyland, or the child of divorced parents, who is taken, endlessly, to movies and amusement parks.

When sadness is denied expression, anger and anxiety are the frequent result, and persons with mental retardation are actively discouraged from expression of these emotions. The person may be redirected, or may be encouraged to "walk it off," rather than express or discuss it. This issue must be addressed with caregivers (Levitas & Gilson, 1989); systems that deal with persons with mental retardation may routinely define the expression of emotion as a problem, whereas the therapist will want to help the patient to begin to experience anxiety, sadness, anger, and guilt as signals and clues to the person's inner life and as reactions to the world. Many persons with mental retardation must experience permission to express, or even feel, an emotion. The only concrete way to help a person do this is by hearing emotional reactions, and by helping to test their validity. To simply repeat reassurances that it is alright to express anger is very often not enough; much more useful in furthering the alliance are such expressions as, "That would make me angry, too," or even, "That once happened to me and I felt the same way." Only in this way can the therapist develop enough of an alliance to confront inappropriate reactions. Some patients may ask directly if a particular feeling is legitimate or permissible.

Others may do so by asking the therapist, for example, "Do you enjoy sex?" To reply by saying, "The question is, do you?" is to miss the retarded person's plea for clarification of whether it is normal to enjoy sex - and guarantees a guarded answer. Such redirection is not experienced by the Mediated Self of a person with mental retardation as a message that it is his or her feelings that are important; rather, it emphasizes for him or her the gulf between the lives of patient and therapist, and reinforces reaction and transference feelings of therapist omniscience and omnipotence.

The experience of emotions as problems, rather than as signals, if not recognized and addressed, can become a major source of resistance in psychotherapy. Resistance most frequently takes the form of decreasing autonomy and a return to earlier maladaptive behavior (Szymanski, 1980). Here, knowledge of the patient's true capabilities is crucial. For most people, some degree of dependency is normal. Therefore, part of the work of analyzing this resistance is an assessment of the capacity of the important people in the patient's life to tolerate or even enjoy the patient's new emotional expressiveness. Educative and therapeutic work may need to be done by the therapist or by the therapist and patient together, with family members or other caregivers. Where this is unavailing, it is legitimate and necessary to make it plain to the patient, in as nonjudgmental a way as possible, the limitations of caregivers. This may take the form of discussing with the patient that, sadly, he or she can talk to the therapist about things in ways that will not be tolerated by others in his or her environment. A search can then begin for alternatives.

The challenge inherent in such "educative" work is to know when the work is complete, and when persistent seeking of personal information, inability to share feelings or experience therapeutic intervention as nonjudgmental represents transference. The most reliable indicator is the return of these phenomena after a period of apparent comfort, often signaled by countertransference discomfort with the patient. The therapist can then confront the patient's return to an earlier way of relating and begin to inquire into why this might be happening. This brings us to a discussion of transference issues as such, their use and resolution.

Transference and Countertransference Issues

Recognition of transference phenomena, like almost everything else about psychotherapy, relies upon the therapist's empathy. From this emerges, first, an appreciation of the patient's pattern of relating, then an appreciation of the patient's pattern of experiencing and feeling. Knowledge of the subculture of retardation can take the therapist only so far in understanding a particular patient's variation on the familiar themes. There is no substitute for empathic listening. Everyone has his or her own way of experiencing and expressing the familiar material of life, and interventions are only of use to the patient if couched in those individual terms. Empathic response to transference material most often begins as a countertransference response, a feeling from the therapist's own past inspired by the patient's present responses.

Szymanski (1980) refers to unconscious guilt at not being able to cure the patient's mental retardation, leading to unconscious idealization of the patient. An equally likely source of this countertransference trap is the transference idealization, which begins with experiencing the therapist as an omniscient, omnipotent teacher, progressing to an idealized parent. Perpetuation of the idealization must be avoided. The idealization can be too gratifying, and compliance plays such a large part in the lives and survival of people with mental retardation that the useful skepticism of patients without mental retardation, which enables them to confront the validity of our interpretations, is absent. A gap may grow between what the patient is saying and what he is doing, a gap that may only become apparent if the therapist is in close touch with the patient's caregivers. Countertransference idealization of the patient is a risk here, leading to expectations the patient cannot hope to meet (a risk often compounded by a similar response to the patient by advocates, family or counselors, often taking the form of feeling that all interventions are somehow limiting to the patient).

The idealization may also cause fear in the therapist of being unable to meet the patient's idealized expectations, or of being drained by the attempt; in this case, there may be a countertransference denigration of the patient and his abilities. Among therapists, this may take the form of a feeling that they must (or that the patient will want them to) cure the mental retardation. Since this cannot be done, it becomes a reason to avoid or withdraw from the patient. A version of this response (based upon a mistaken belief that the problems of persons with mental retardation stem entirely from their mental retardation, and thus that their lives never can be, or never can be made, happy) may be the aversion many mental health professionals have for working with persons with mental retardation (Levitas & Gilson, 1989).

A similar reaction and counter-reaction may be set up when the agency or family, who has referred the patient for therapy, has idealized expectations of the therapist. Caregivers may expect that, just like the physical therapist, the psychotherapist will manipulate the patient in ways that will quickly eliminate the problem behavior (Lott, 1970; Szymanski, 1980). The therapist must rely upon contact with the caregivers, educating them early to the workings and values of psychotherapy. The therapist may then avoid the pitfalls of succumbing to the caregivers' idealization, and the risk of taking on the task of "adjusting" the person with mental retardation to a perhaps noxious reality; or of feeling helpless to effect any sort of change, and withdrawing from or becoming angry at the patient's real needs (Levitas & Gilson, 1989).

The therapist is in danger of becoming a rescuer, and it is often difficult - given the frightful plight of some people with mental retardation - to decide for oneself whether one's actions are reality-based or are manifestations of counterreaction or countertransference. The best guide appears to be common humanity, on one hand ("Am I doing too little?"), and, on the other hand, an awareness that one has gone too far if one has, or is trying to, become the patient's caregiver, or fight battles for him or her that the patient is capable of fighting on his/her own (Levitas & Gilson, 1989).

Resolution of idealizing transferences always begins with an empathic understanding of the patient's needs and fears, and the clarification that such an idealized relationship serves to avoid fears of failure and growth toward a sometimes frightening autonomy. Since the denigrating countertransference originates in the therapist's fears of not being able to meet the patient's neurotic needs, such clarification is the road to resolution.

A special form of idealized transference is the emotional over attachment popularly referred to as a "crush." A patient with mental retardation may express a wish to make the therapist - who may be the only person in the patient's life who truly listens, and who values the patient for him or herself - into a real love object. It is usually a mistake to regard this as oedipal transference; that is, a fantasy based upon the seduction of the therapist. It is just as likely to originate in the genuine lack of empathic human relationships in the patient's life. Successful intervention begins with a discussion, or search, with the patient for other sources of caring, understanding relationships in his or her life, including, most emphatically, relationships among peers. Only then can one confront and clarify for the patient that a continuation of the crush, to the exclusion of real relationships, is a way of avoiding risk and autonomy (Levitas & Gilson, 1989).

Negative transference may take the form of anger at or envy of the therapist, with resulting denigration, insult, silence or acting-out. Countertransference rejection or guilt may result, with efforts to either end the therapy, on the grounds that the patient is now sufficiently assertive or is unresponsive, indulge the patient's angry or envious demands for a premature autonomy at which he or she cannot succeed, or engage caregivers in setting unnecessary limits. Empathic exploration of the sources of envy and anger in the patient's life is the necessary course, and it can be painful. Such anger and envy is frequently based less upon the therapist's material advantages (which the patient may note, calling forth countertransference guilt) than upon life experiences of perceived rejection which the patient attributes to having mental retardation. Parental anger, disappointment of all kinds, divorce, and out of home placement may be correctly attributed or misattributed by the patient to the fact of his or her retardation. Acknowledgment that parents - and therapists - are subject to this sort of failure may be necessary before proceeding to examine the grounds for any individual patient's sense of such rejection.

The angry/envious transference may take the form of frustration of the therapist's efforts by repeated failure, as if to say, "You cannot make me better/grow/perform, just as my other caregivers could not make me normal." Countertransference frustration can take the form of wishes to be rid of the patient, to be revenged, or to prove the patient incapable. Complete assessment before beginning therapy here proves its worth; countertransference fantasies of repeating complete neuropsychological testing can be the earliest clue that this transference/countertransference response is underway. Exploration of the fantasy of being made "normal" is the route to resolution.

A form of negative transference with a potentially serious countertransference trap is presented by the patient who experiences therapeutic interventions as controlling or engulfing. This may be seen in patients who have a particularly strong need to deny (for fear of caregiver rejection) any reference to themselves as affected by a disability. Such patients may react to any such reference with rage and demands for increased autonomy, and to any therapeutic intervention as such a reference. Therapists and caregivers may respond with an "indulgent countertransference;" agreeing to the patient's demands for increased autonomy despite serious misgivings; the patient responds to this as if to a rejection (as if caregivers have said, "Go ahead, I don't care what you do").

In the end, the task of transference resolution for the patient is one of self-acceptance. There remains the resolution of the dependency upon the therapist is relinquishment of the fantasy of an ideal parent.

Resolution of Dependency

Resolution of dependency issues begins in verbal resolution of the transference, but must also take the form of real action and practice, both to fuel the exploration of transference issues and to bring them to final resolution. Szymanski (1980) begins to address this issue with the addition of concrete activities in the community (for example, going to a store) to the list of therapeutic interventions.

As therapy progresses, confrontation of the patient's expectation of being cared for may increase; interpretation alone will not eliminate it. The goal of therapy is for the patient to take some control of behavior and return to the previous level of functioning or better. The therapist will be in a position to use events such as Individual Educational Program and Individual Habilitation Program conferences, which by law must take place at least annually, and may be convened more frequently, as graded experiences in autonomy. The therapist can offer several flexible alternatives for participation in the meeting. One can offer to speak for the patient, making agreements about what will and won't be said. One can offer to be physically present, but at all times encourage the patient to speak for him/herself. One can offer to be in the next room, or available by telephone if this helps the patient to express him/herself confidently, or to get caregivers to listen. One can offer to be physically present, but limit interventions to observations, confrontations, and clarifications of caregiver responses (Levitas & Gilson, 1989). This activity is, of course, combined with discussion of the outcomes during the therapeutic sessions.

Termination

It is often more difficult for the therapist to terminate than it is for the patient. This can be a function of the transference/countertransference issues described above. The therapist, if he or she has adopted a parental role or stance, may feel uncomfortable with the risk of returning the patient to fend for himself. The failure to be able to terminate may reflect an unconscious inability to trust a person with mental retardation to function independently.

If the therapist has in any way helped to empower the patient, helped to link him or her with other sources of support, power, and relationships in the community, and if the therapist has educated family and other caregivers to the needs, strengths, and inner life of the patient, termination will occur naturally. Termination may be the last step the therapist may help the patient to take in resolution of the transference.

The process of termination may be modified to take into account the patient's more concrete functioning. The patient may need a shorter time to express sadness and farewell, and to practice application of the confidence he or she has acquired and begun to feel. Some patients may find it useful to have final sessions at longer than accustomed intervals. Others may want to talk about termination for a session or two, then practice by agreeing to meet with the therapist in a month, to assess life without therapy - and most likely terminate at that point. Szymanski (1980) notes that vacations and other therapist absences are useful transition points in the termination process, as well as useful predictors of patient response to termination.

Patients with mental retardation need to be reminded that they are welcome to return for further work at any time. They may state outright that which often remains an unspoken wish among patients without mental retardation - a desire to occasionally contact the therapist about good news or events in their lives. Where this wish is spontaneous, to have such contacts is not in any way condescending or undermining of the patient's autonomy. They will be as rewarding for the therapist as they are for the patient (Levitas & Gilson, 1989).

Transference/Countertransference Issues with Patients with Severe and Profound Mental Retardation

In the United States severe and profound mental retardation have been regarded as barriers to psychodynamic psychotherapy. Elsewhere they have been regarded, rather, as a frontier. Gaedt (1995) notes the theoretical basis for psychodynamic treatment of this population in the integration of ego psychology, object relations theory, and the observations of the growing field of infant psychiatry, adding a new category of disorder: "persisting developmental deficit," characterized by compulsive re-enactment of expressions of a pathological identification with an ambivalently-experienced caregiver in early development The repetitive behavior is a transference reaction repeated with all caregivers and peers. The repetition is compulsive because it is a re-enactment of "emotional experiences which have become personally important to the participating persons" to the point that they are guarantors of personality integrity.

If this is so, according to Gaedt, explanations of such repetitive behavior, usually grounded in theories of learned responses or biologically-based Obsessive-Compulsive Disorder, ignore motivation entirely; this in turn may explain the failure of both behavioral intervention and anti-obsessive medication to successfully address such behavior as repetitive aggression and self-injury. Gaedt raises the interesting and painful possibility that suppressing such behaviors with drugs and behavioral strategies while ignoring their importance to the patient's maintenance of a sense of self risks long-term worsening whatever the short-term outcome in reduced physical injury. The patient "only experiences consistent and mostly negative responses while interacting on the basis of his/her distorted value system with his/her caregivers...he/she will merely be confirmed in his/her distorted affective evaluation. He/she is not offered a way out of this distorted experiencing of the world." Psychodynamic understanding and therapy are necessary to adequate treatment. The behavior must be interpreted so that it can be given up and development continued to the furthest point possible.

Persons with severe and profound mental retardation will always require some caregiver supervision, so that resolution of dependency is less a matter of discontinuation than of moving to a less neurotic and painful way of relating to caregivers by way of a corrective emotional experience (Gaedt, 1995). Sinason (1992) describes the experience as provided in the course of the interpretation of the patient's behavior in much the same way that a young child's play behavior is interpreted. Since the pathological behavior is all a transference manifestation, the task of the therapist is to understand the non-verbal communication through transference empathy, i.e. to make therapeutic use of the Mediated Self.

Sinason (1982) poignantly explains this phenomenon:

> Bion (1959) explored the concept of the analyst as the container for the patient's intolerable experiences, just as the good-enough parent is the container of her baby's nameless fears. The younger the child or the more severely handicapped the child or adult, the greater the need to work more by understanding the counter-transference or the nature of the communication the patient has sent to the therapist to be held (p. 81).

Sinason likens the process to a mother's understanding of her infant's need only from its cry and the resulting countertransference understanding. The distress is transmuted by the greater ego resources of the therapist into countertransference empathy, and through interpretation is returned to the patient in bearable form. Pathology based in previous caregivers' inability to tolerate the patient or his/her distress is thus corrected.

Three preconditions must be met for this approach to be successful. The therapist's relationship with and understanding of the patient must be based upon thorough and accurate history, and the therapist must be prepared to make use of this information whatever its source (p.126) and to present all interpretations as tentative, to be verified by the patient (p.251). Secondly, the therapist must constantly carry out rigorous self-analysis to filter out of the communication counter-transference and counter-reaction to the patient's damaged state, real hurt, and the therapist's own fantasies about it (p.81). Finally, the interpretations are couched in the correct mood and tone, since so much of the communication will be carried by these extra-linguistic features.

Sinason and Gaedt both stress the importance of work with the other caregivers in the patient's life. Reorientation of caregivers to a psychodynamic understanding of the patient's repetitive behaviors is crucial to encouraging and maintaining the patient's new growth and development. "They would recognize which role they play in the transference relationship and how they could make use of their relationship in a "corrective" emotional experience'" (Gaedt, 1995). Sinason (1992) notes the necessity of the use of restraints and other forms of protection from harm by caregiving staff not trained in this way (p.114), both from the standpoint of patient protection and from the standpoint of transference/countertransference problems with caregivers; she would confine the therapeutic work where self-injury is the medium of communication from the patient to the period of the actual therapeutic session where staff are untrained.

The psychodynamic understanding of and approach to the repetitive behaviors of persons with severe and profound mental retardation offers a rich area for advancement in humane and enlightened treatment, to which empathy and understanding of transference/countertransference issues is central. It is difficult to imagine such a labor-intensive and highly skilled approach being undertaken on a large scale at the present period of cutbacks in services to precisely this patient population. Gaedt raises the disturbing possibility that our current approaches, like the institutional practices that spawned them, merely perpetuate the problems and the pain they cause. We can only hope that this research will be pursued, and if fruitful applied on a larger scale.

Acknowledgments: This chapter is gratefully dedicated to Dr. Robert Sovner, friend and colleague, for his years of support and comradeship: Thank you.

References

Aman, M.G. (1991). *Assessing psychopathology and behavior problems in persons with mental retardation: A review of available instruments*. Rockville, MD: US Department of Health and Human Services.

Asch, A., & Fine, M. (Eds.). (1988). Moving disability beyond stigma. [Special issue]. *Journal of Social Issues*, 44(1).

Beck, H.L. (1962). Casework with parents of mentally retarded children. *American Journal of Orthopsychiatry 32,* 870-77.

Bion, W. (1959). Attacks on linking. *International Journal of Psychoanalysis, 40*, 308-315.

Gaedt, C. (1995). Psychotherapeutic approaches in the treatment of mental illness and behavioral disorders in mentally retarded people: The significance of a psychoanalytic perspective. *Journal of Intellectual Disability Research 39*, 233-239.

Gilson, S.F., Baskind, F., & Bricout, J. (1998). Social work's perspective on disability and our reality: Families and society. *Journal of Contemporary Human Services, 79*, 188-196.

Hahn, H. (1993). The politics of physical differences: Disability and discrimination. In M. Nagler (Ed.), *Perspectives on disability* (2nd ed., pp. 37-42). Palo Alto, CA: Health Markets Research.

Levitas, A.S., & Gilson, S.F. (1994). Psychosocial development of children and adolescents with mild and moderate mental retardation. In N. Bouras (Ed.), *Mental health in mental retardation: Recent advances and practices* (pp. 34-45). Cambridge: Cambridge University Press.

Levitas, A.S., & Gilson, S.F. (1990). Toward the developmental understanding of the impact of mental retardation on assessment of psychopathology. In E. Dibble & D.G. Gray (Eds.), *Assessment of behavior problems in persons with mental retardation living in the community* (pp. 71-106). Rockville, MD: National Institute of Mental Health.

Levitas, A.S., & Gilson, S.F. (1989). Psychodynamic psychotherapy with mildly and moderately retarded patients. In R. Fletcher & F. Menolascino (Eds.), *Mental retardation and mental illness: Assessment, treatment and service for the dually diagnosed* (pp. 71-109). Lexington, MA: Lexington Books.

Lott, G. (1970). Psychotherapy of the mentally retarded: Values and cautions. In F.J. Menolascino (Ed.), *Psychiatric approaches to mental retardation* (pp.227-250). New York: Basic Books.

Rogers, C.R., & Dyamond, R.F. (1954). *Psychotherapy and personality change*. Chicago: University of Chicago Press.

Ruesch, J., & Kees, W. (1956). *Nonverbal communication*. Los Angeles: University of California Press.

Sinason, V. (1992). *Mental handicap and the human condition: New approaches from the Tavistock*. London: Free Association Books.

Sternlicht, M. (1966). Psychotherapeutic procedure with the retarded. In E. Nurmad (Ed.), *International Review of Research in Mental Retardation, 10,* 279-354). New York: Academic Press.

Sternlicht, M. (1965). Psychotherapy techniques useful with mentally retarded: A review and critique. *Psychiatric Quarterly, 39,* 84-90.

Szymanski, L.S. (1980). Individual psychotherapy with retarded persons. In L. Szymanski & M. Tanguay (Eds.), *Emotional disorders of mentally retarded persons: Assessment, treatment, and consultation* (pp. 131-147). Baltimore: University Park Press.

Wehman, P., Gilson, S. F., & Tusler, A. (Eds.). (1997). Disability empowerment. [Special issue]. *Journal of Vocational Rehabilitation, 9*(1).

Zola, I. K. (1993). Self, identity and the naming question: Reflections on the language of disability. In M. Nagler (Ed.), *Perspectives on disability* (2nd ed., pp. 15-23). Palo Alto, CA: Health Markets Research.

CHAPTER FOUR

GROUP THERAPY FOR PEOPLE WITH MENTAL RETARDATION

Daniel J. Tomasulo, Ph.D., T.E.P., C.G.P.

Despite evidence of effectiveness and recommendations by researchers to use a group method, group psychotherapy for people with mental retardation is usually not considered as a viable therapeutic modality. Historically, the research on this matter showed that people with mental retardation could not profit from insight oriented interactive therapy because they lacked specific cognitive abilities thought necessary for therapeutic change. Although many clinicians have not regarded people with mental retardation as suitable candidates for any form of psychotherapy (Hurley, 1989; Hurley, Pfadt, Tomasulo, & Gardner, 1996), there are many case reports on the effectiveness of individual psychotherapy (Hurley, 1989) as well as for group psychotherapy (Pfadt, 1991). Psychotherapy for people with mental retardation has been most effective when a directive style with structured sessions is used (Hurley, 1989; Hurley & Hurley, 1986, 1988; Fletcher, 1984; Hingsburger, 1987; Tomasulo, 1992; Tomasulo, Keller, & Pfadt, 1995; Hurley et al., 1996). Additionally the use of active/interactive techniques is often preferred as they stimulate more sensory and affective modes of learning than the verbal modality alone (Hurley et al.; Tomasulo, 1994). While a lack of cognitive abilities may be the primary reason that psychotherapy is overlooked as a treatment modality for people with mental retardation, there have been a series of erroneous assumptions on the part of practitioners. Consider the following major suppositions:

1. Since many developmentally disabled people are not verbal (or have difficulty verbalizing) they are thought to be unable to produce clues to regulating their behavior.
2. The secondary disabilities that often accompany people with mental retardation (short attention span, auditory and visual handicaps, seizure activity, etc.) are thought to provide insurmountable obstacles to interactive group therapy.
3. People with mental retardation are thought to lack the cognitive ability to profit from insight into the causes and consequences of their behavior.
4. Many practitioners understand the emotional disorders displayed by people with mental retardation as a side effect of a bio-chemical brain dysfunction. As such they feel there is little which psychotherapy can offer.
5. Somehow the emotional and behavioral problems of people with mental retardation are understood as being the result of mental illness <u>or</u> behavior disorders. With such elementary discriminations only psychopharma-

cological or behavioral treatments alone are sought. The use of psychotherapy to help ameliorate these problems is rarely considered.

People with chronic psychiatric problems have had more exposure to group treatment than people with mental retardation. However, with the advent of the "dual diagnosis" awareness for people with mental retardation/mental health (MR/MH) problems, the need for improved treatment procedures in group therapy has been recognized. The Interactive Behavior Therapy (IBT) format is an adaptation and enhancement of techniques and process known to be effective with people with mental retardation as well as those with a dual diagnosis.

The reality is that even if an astute and aware clinician were to recommend psychotherapy for people with the above noted problems, the task of finding someone knowledgeable and competent to deliver such services would often be a difficult job. Although more and more providers are beginning groups and developing their group skills, the reality is group psychotherapy is the least often recommended and practiced form of treatment for people with mental retardation. One other reason why group therapy is the least used therapy for people with mental retardation (in addition to the reasons listed above), may be that the dissemination of information on how to do such counseling was limited by the scarcity of research and training literature showing which method(s) were effective. This is to say that although there may have been indications that group therapy could be possible, the volume of such information was not sufficient to offset the assumptions of practitioners.

The time has come for greater attention to be given to the group process. To begin with, using group counseling for people with mental retardation makes good clinical and economic sense. Consider the advantages of using a group format:

1. The skills to run an effective group can be taught in a brief period of time (2-3 months for a novice and considerably less for the more experienced).
2. In the same amount of time it takes to run a teaching based skill-training group (which evolved rather than a therapeutic group), a more richly interactive group can take place through facilitation rather than teaching.
3. More people can be served in a group counseling format than can be served in an individual setting.
4. It can be argued that the treatment in a group is more effective than individual counseling.
5. On all pay scales the cost to an individual for group psychotherapy is cheaper than individual therapy.
6. Specific topics may target selected groups for particular problems (anger management groups, sex offender groups, bereavement groups, job readiness, etc.). In this way people with similar issues may gain support in ways not possible in individual counseling.
7. This kind of peer support is not limited to homogeneous groups. Interper-

sonal support from peers struggling with different issues is not available in any other format.

Role Playing

One of the longest-standing techniques in training, education, and therapy is role-playing. Role-playing is used in nearly every phase of human development to teach and model behavior. Parents use role play and children use it extensively during free play throughout early development. Within the field of counseling a more specific and elaborated use of role-playing has taken place through the development of Psychodrama (Blatner, 1996).

Psychodrama is an action-oriented therapy and technique, which endeavors to express a condition or offer a solution to a situation through the combined efforts of a group . In fact, self-help groups and the systematic use of role playing in education and training are actually descendants of the Psychodramatic method (Blatner, 1988).

The use of role playing for training, education, simulation, dramatic presentation, skill development and therapy is so pervasive that it is woven into the fabric of our society so seamlessly that it is barely recognizable as a science, art form, and acquired skill. Its natural process is at once so familiar and so agreeable that people use it in their programs without the slightest hesitation as to form. It is as though there is an attitude of: "It's only role-playing - I know how to do that." While the quality of most role-playing may achieve adequacy, the depth and breath of using of active/interactive techniques is usually missed. While there seems to be a fair degree of support for the use of role playing, there is relatively little in the way of guidelines for the development of role-playing activities for potential leaders. This section will introduce the reader to the theory and technique of using the "double", a specific role playing technique particularly useful in helping individuals with developmental disabilities. Although role playing and Psychodramatic techniques such as the double may be used in individual psychotherapy, this section will look at the ways in which these techniques may be used to enhance the dynamics of a therapy group for adolescents and adults with mental retardation.

Psychodrama and Sociodramatic theory (Steinberg & Garcia, 1989; Blatner, 1988) offers the most widely accepted format for facilitation role playing techniques within a group setting. The use of these techniques in groups for people with mental retardation has been modified to accommodate the unique needs of this population. The Interactive-Behavioral Group Therapy model (Tomasulo, 1992; Tomasulo, et al., 1995; Tomasulo, 1998) uses a 45-to-60-minute, four-stage format to facilitate the use of action techniques for people with mental retardation. It uses this brief format for the following reasons:

1. The condensed time demands reduces the possibility of exhausting the members' abilities to remain physically and emotionally present.

2. The time frame keeps the co-facilitator(s) more focused on their task.
3. The shorter meeting time than traditional groups fits into the schedules of most hospitals, agencies, residences, vocational settings, and schools.
4. If billing 3rd party payment it provides a standard and acceptable time period for reimbursement.

The model combines theoretically sound techniques for activating therapeutic factors from the field of Psychodrama (Tomasulo, 1994) with some modifications specific to people with dual diagnosis (e.g., the orientation and affirmation stages). The four stages of this model are: (a) orientation, (b) warm-up and sharing, (c) enactment, and (d) affirmation.

STAGES OF THE IBT MODEL

Stage 1: Orientation & Cognitive Networking

In a group for individuals with mental retardation, many secondary disabilities as well as the primary cognitive deficits inhibit interaction between members. For this reason the facilitator works to engage the members in "cognitive networking" during the initial orientation stage. Having members repeat what was said to them, turn toward the person speaking, acknowledge what was said, and/or in some way participate in the group process through interaction is the goal of this first stage. If the members fail to attend to each other, any other therapeutic, corrective, or instructional goals within the group will not be realized. Additionally, the orientation stage provides a familiar beginning signal for the members to help them realize the group has begun.

This stage was designed to help with the initial difficulties encountered in establishing a group with the potential for therapeutic factors to emerge. Poor eye contact, difficulty with short-term recognition or memory, impaired hearing, delayed responding, confusion, echolalia, inattention, distractibility, speech impediments and hyperactivity are just some of the obstacles to interaction among members. Therefore, it becomes a primary function of the facilitators to stay focused on the development of cognitive networking between the members. This is a direct effort to establish basic interactions between and among the group's members by having them repeat, acknowledge or otherwise support what another member in the group said. Physically orienting towards the person speaking, looking at them and echoing back what was heard are central elements to the activity. This process begins in the orientation stage but will continue throughout the group. Without such rudimentary interaction there is a diminished opportunity for therapeutic factors to emerge and be reinforced. As such, the facilitator(s) assisting members in interacting with each other and participating in the group process characterize the orientation stage. This is the goal of this first stage. If the members fail to attend to each other, any other therapeutic, corrective, or instructional goals within the group will not be realized.

Stage 2: Warm-up & Sharing

In the warm-up and sharing stage the facilitator invites the members to speak about themselves within the group. This is a process-driven group, and as such, the content of their presentations is of less importance. In other words, the facilitator's concern is with the dynamics of the group, and not, necessarily, what the participants are saying. The facilitator's job is to pay attention to the nature of the interactions between the various members. During this second stage the group members take turns making their self-disclosures, and the cognitive networking begun in the orientation stage is continued. For example, the facilitator may ask the member who has just finished speaking to select the next member to go. In this way, members are again encouraged to pay attention to and interact with each other rather than with the facilitator exclusively. Following this level of participation the facilitator will then ask the members if any of them has a problem to work on in the group. It is during this deeper level of sharing that the members will experience a greater sense of emotional involvement within the group. The group becomes more cohesive, and the stage is set for action to take place.

The second stage of the group ushers in more intimate interactions between members. This is referred to as the warm-up and sharing stage because we are "warming-up" to the enactment. We are "warming-up" to being together and learning from each other. Notice before an athletic event: the athletes stretch, bounce and slowly get themselves ready for participation. They try to get themselves prepared to perform at level of competency that may not attainable without a warm-up. Even the computer gets itself ready for the tasks at hand. A preparation is necessary for maximum effectiveness. Group leaders often start with an agenda and content when the members are too often ill prepared. In the warm-up and sharing stage the facilitator invites the members to speak within the group. As mentioned this is a process-driven group, and as such, the content of their presentations is of less importance. In other words, the facilitator's concern is with the dynamics of the group. Has everyone had a chance to speak? Who has been chosen whom to speak after them? Who has accurately heard what was said? Each of these concerns far outweighs the content of the group. Indeed the message/content of the group will be lost without sufficient preparation of the participants. The facilitator's job is to pay attention to the nature of the interactions between the various members. During this second stage the group members take turns making their self-disclosures, and the cognitive networking begun in the orientation stage is continued. For example, the facilitator may ask the member who has just finished speaking to select the next member to go. In this way, members are again encouraged to pay attention to and interact with each other rather than with the facilitator exclusively. Following this level of participation the facilitator can then ask the participants to share something from their week. Once each person has had a chance to go the facilitator will then ask the members if any of them has a problem to work on in the group. It is during this deeper level of sharing that the members will experience a greater sense of emotional involvement within the group. The group becomes more cohesive, and the stage is set for action to take place.

Stage 3: Enactment

Psychodrama is a particular type of group psychotherapy that involves both theory and techniques. In fact, Psychodrama is the original form of group work developed by the creator of the term "group therapy", Jacob Moreno, M.D. Over the years techniques from psychodrama (reflecting issues unique to an individual's life) and sociodrama (issues which reflect a collective concern) have been used with people with mental retardation . However the primary use of role-playing was for role training. More specifically, these techniques were used almost exclusively for social-skills training rather than for the purpose of counseling; teaching and training rather than facilitating therapeutic interactions were the aim of social-skill groups.

The teachers of social skills groups foster interaction between themselves and the participants rather than between and among the participants. Since the emphasis was on teaching a skill, the attention had to be focused on the teacher/trainer. In the Interactive-Behavioral format the emphasis is on interaction between the participants for the purpose of creating a therapeutic environment. As such there is a major shift from a teaching/training model to a peer support/interaction model where behaviors having therapeutic value are reinforced as a way of strengthening viable group processes.

There is a graphic description of the degree to which a typical group may expect to emotional involvement from its participants (as shown in Figure 1). In a 45 minute to 1-hour group there is likely to be greater involvement as the group moves towards the Enactment Stage. The readiness of the members of the group to take part in the action portion of the group allows them to have greater concentration, presence, and emotional involvement. In this way the format and process of the Interactive-Behavioral model lends itself toward creating an opportunity for a "teachable moment" when the participants are able to take part in a way that allows for learning to take place.

It is during this enactment stage when techniques such as role-playing and the "double" are used. The issues presented in the warm-up and sharing stage are formulated into an interactive sequence with the help of the facilitator. Although only certain group members may take part in the enactment, the entire group's focus of attention is on the action taking place. Within the Enactment Stage there are a number of techniques used to stimulate interaction between group members. One of the most useful of those techniques is the double (Tomasulo,1994). Broadly stated, a double is a role played by one or more group members to give voice to the feelings and thoughts of another member who is struggling with a given problem. The use of the double can be a tremendous asset in groups for people with mental retardation, chronic psychiatric illness and dual diagnoses (MR/MH).

The double has three purposes: (a) providing emotional support, (b) giving emotional expression, and (c) reorganizing perceptions.

The process and techniques used in doubling include: (a) speaking the unspoken (what the person needs to say but is not saying), (b) exaggerating, (c) minimizing, (d) introducing alternatives, (e) restating, (f) amplifying (highlighting the key part of the statement, (g) verbalizing the resistance (why the person doesn't want to say something), (h) introducing paradoxes (see the section below on paired doubles), and (i) clarifying (see the section below on correcting the double).

Using the Double for Support

A great deal of progress can be achieved through the use of the double. It provides you freedom to add features to the group process that would not be possible without action techniques. Typically, the double is positioned behind the protagonist (the identified person of interest) and slightly to one side. The protagonist can be sitting or standing, and the double can assume the same physical stance as the protagonist. Assuming the same physical stance as the protagonist allows the double to "warm-up" to the internal state of the protagonist. This type of warm-up allows the person playing the double to mimic the protagonist in a way that gives clues to the internal state. All this, however, is but a readiness to understand the protagonist in a way that will provide an isomorphic condition that matches the internal state of the protagonist. This condition allows the emotional expression, emotional support or the reorganizing of perceptions to emerge more naturally. If the double can create an atmosphere that the protagonist feels supported and understood, the opportunity for change is greatly enhanced. It is important for the facilitator to arrange for the protagonist to be seated and for the double(s) to stand behind his or her chair. The position behind the protagonist is symbolic of the supportive position of the parents. Our parents are the first people to think for us. We become who we are largely because of the influence left on us by our caregivers. When the therapist stands behind the protagonist, he/she is representing a non-confrontational and more supportive position.

Contra-indications

The primary contra-indication for the position behind the protagonist is when it increases anxiety (as it usually does with people who are paranoid). In these instances the doubling can be done from another position such as the front or side.

Choice of the Double

Choosing the double can happen in one of five ways:
1. The facilitator can chose the double.
2. The protagonist can chose the double from the group.

3. A group member can volunteer.
4. The facilitator can do the doubling.
5. The protagonist can double himself or herself.

Doubles may be single, in pairs (to allow for contrast or amplification/restatement) or in multiples (usually done to help the protagonist experience such therapeutic factors as acceptance and universality with their fellow members). The emergence of a protagonist within the group indicates that one person has presented a problem that is significant enough for exploration within the group. There are many parameters which determine the selection of the protagonist which have been discussed elsewhere (Blatner, 1989; Tomasulo, 1992). In most cases the protagonist presents a situation which reflects a deficiency or an interpersonal or intrapsychic conflict. This deficiency or conflict is often the central issue of the drama.

Common Errors

Perhaps one of the most common errors a group facilitator makes when first using action techniques is to have the protagonist engage in an encounter or rehearsal at the onset of the action. While it is certainly appropriate for a group facilitator to use role-playing to rehearse a new behavior or to act out an encounter, it is often not the best place to start. While such a role-play may, on the surface, seem reasonable, it may actually result in the distancing of the protagonist from the group (if he or she is not ready for such an event) or alienating those members of the group who cannot relate to the encounter. Additionally, the protagonist may be able to change his or her behavior in the group but, if not adequately supported, it is unlikely that the member will be able to carry over the newly learned behaviors into his or her environment. The solution to this dilemma may come from using the double as a means of support. Creating an atmosphere of support is probably the most important condition the facilitator can help create. If you are going to make an error it is best to make it on the side of having too much support rather than too little. Remember, trust and safety are the cornerstone of the group. The double can help create this ambiance for the protagonist.

Stage 4: Affirmation

Finally, in the affirmation stage the facilitator validates the participation of each of the members in the group. This is done with specific attention to the therapeutic factors (Yalom, 1995; Bloch & Crouch, 1985). Each member is verbally acknowledged for his or her interactive contributions to the group. Specifically, if someone displays a trait that is interactive and reflective of a therapeutic factor, it will get reinforced. In one experiment on the IBT model (Tomasulo et at. 1995) the raters were briefed in the stage format of the model and were asked to note which interactions in the group could be considered examples of therapeutic factors. Eight factors were chosen for observation: (a) acceptance/cohesion, (b) universality, (c) altruism, (d) installation of hope,

(e) guidance, (f) vicarious learning modeling, (g) catharsis, and (h) imparting of information.

Twelve sessions run weekly with both a high functioning group (mild mental retardation) and a low functioning group (moderately mentally retarded) using the Interactive-Behavioral model revealed the presence of all eight of the therapeutic factors. (See Table 1).

Table 1. Reliability Ratings on Therapeutic Factors

Factor	Rating
1. Acceptance/cohesion	.86
2. Universality	.90
3. Altruism	.76
4. Installation of hope	.86
5. Guidance	1.00
6. Vicarious Learning/Modeling	.45
7. Catharsis	.96
8. Imparting of information	.91

As noted earlier the shift towards group counseling from skill training groups may require that the content of the group become secondary to its process. The IBT model has enjoyed wide usage. To a large degree this is due to the fact that the model describes a process taken from well-established principles in group psychotherapy which have been modified for people with mental retardation. This allows the group process to use various curricula. As an example the IBT model has been used in: anger management, AIDS awareness training, relationship counseling, sexual abuse avoidance training as well as therapy for offenders and victims of sexual abuse (Razza & Tomasulo, 1996a, 1996b, 1996c) mental health counseling, vocational readiness, behavior management, travel training, independent living readiness, sex education, socialization, educational readiness, parent-child education, birth control, advocacy groups, and others. Such a broad base use of the model would seem to indicate that the four stage process of the group is more essential to the functioning of the group than the content. The presence of therapeutic factors within the group sets the stage for corrective work to be done. Future research should focus on the validity of the process of the groups run for people with mental retardation. Hereafter, researchers may focus on these or other aspects of traditional group therapy which they can identify happening in their specialized groups. While this data indicates that some essential elements of the group process are present in this model, more research is needed to demonstrate the viability of the group process with other elements and other models.

The cognitive networking which began in the Orientation stage continues throughout the four stages. This helps to insure what is being worked on is being taken in by the participants. In general terms the Orientation as well as the Warm-up and Sharing stages are relatively tedious for the facilitators. The task of weaving together the fabric of thoughts and words is often not very stimulating. This is the foundation upon which nearly everything else in group must rest. The time invested into these two stages is necessary for any gains to be realized in the second half of the group.

The Affirmation Stage signals the end of the group and serves to slow down the emotional build-up that has taken place during the session. The primary concern of the facilitator is to attend to the emotional needs of the individuals who are being served in the group. The concern is that the issues dealt with during the session have impacted the participants in such a way that they may need more time to absorb the elements of the session. The facilitator may help them by providing additional affirmations. An affirmation helps members identify those components of their participation which are directly tied to therapeutic factors and other interactive features that pertain to their emotional growth. Most often the affirmation stage signifies the need to close down the emotional aspects of participation and allow members to return to their normal routine in a neutral or positive attitude. Towards this end the emotional involvement in the group usually peaks during the Enactment Stage and plateaus during the Affirmation stage. This is different than other models of group therapy where action methods are used. In another model a bell shaped format that has a "Warm-up" stage as the firsthand of the curve, the Enactment Stage as the highest peak of intensity and emotional involvement, and finally the "Sharing" stage, which happens during the final stage of the session and is indicated by the downward slope of the right side of the bell shaped curve. Additionally there is a spiral format that has a funnel-shaped form. This model identifies the intensity of the session located in the center core of the funnel. The beginning of the session is on the perimeter. The session then moves to the center core. Lastly, after the core of the session has been reached, the group must be brought back to the perimeter. These models are helpful in understanding group dynamics. The necessary modification for the IBT model is that facilitators must be mindful of the fact that the groups may stir emotions that may not be expressed in this population. As such, assure the group that they are being provided with an opportunity to "decompress" from the group experience if need be. In these matters it is always better to err on the side of being too cautious. If someone is suspected of having residual feelings from the group, be certain to help them connect to an individual counselor, a staff person or teacher who can be helpful. (The facilitator may also provide counseling). If the facilitator were new to the field it would be important to have supervision with someone who has had more experience.

Transcripts from an Initial IBT Session

The following is a partial transcript of an initial session. This session was the first of a series of five sessions conducted at The Young Adult Institute in New York City for the purpose of making a training video (Tomasulo, 1992). The tape is used in training staff to use the Interactive-Behavioral group model and includes a video manual. The members of the group were unknown to the facilitator prior to the taping.

None of the people participating as members had ever taken part in an Interactive-Behavioral group before. They were somewhat familiar with role-playing and each knew the other members' names. In fact, in this group, the members lived together in a group home.

There were six members in the group: Gretta, Leah, Lenore, David, Cindy and Hollis. All of them were classified as dually diagnosed, meaning they had both mild mental retardation and a psychiatric diagnosis. Also in the group is a co-facilitator, Catrina.

The principles of the Interactive-Behavioral model are demonstrated in this initial group. Each of the stages of the group is identified. Notice that the facilitator takes a highly active, directive approach to running the group. Each interaction is encouraged and facilitated by involvement of the group leader. This type of involvement lessens as the group matures. Indeed in the studies conducted on the Interactive-Behavioral model we have found greater and greater involvement between the members over session as there is less interaction between the facilitator and the members. A pizza dinner was offered to the members of the group each week. Their inclusion in the group was voluntary and permission for us to record the group was obtained. The group is representative of the model and accurately characterizes an initial group interaction. There are two things that make this particular group unique. First is the fact that these are all residents from the same group home. This means that they will need less (perhaps) of an orientation to each other. Usually the work done in these types of groups has a tremendous impact on the members. The members get to work on the issues they have developed during the course of the group meetings in a more direct way. Groups who do not live together have less opportunity to put their new awareness into effect with each other. However they must transfer the skills they learn in group to people they encounter in other settings. Process comments are indicated in bold type. Please note space considerations prohibit a complete transcript. Samples for each stage are shown.

The Orientation Stage

Cognitive networking begins as soon as one person begins speaking.
FACILITATOR: "So what did you hear about this group?"
DAVID: "Well I heard this is a big chance to get into the movies and TV show."
FACILITATOR: "Movies and TV show. Gretta, did you hear what David said?"
GRETTA: "Yes."
LEAH: "I heard."
GRETTA: "To get into movies and TV."
FACILITATOR: "Terrific."

GRETTA: "But I also heard that it was a counseling group."
FACILITATOR: "A counseling group?"
GRETTA: " That's what they told me"
FACILITATOR: "Leah, Did you hear what Gretta said?"
LEAH: "Yeah."
FACILITATOR: "What did she say?"
LENORE: "err... ahhrr, couns...err..."
CINDY: "A counseling group."
LENORE: "A counseling group."
FACILITATOR: " O.K., Good. All right. Maybe what would be good, you guys are listening so well, maybe you could just say your names so that we have all that on tape and we know who is who. You can just say your first names and that will help will help me remember. Who wants to go first?"
DAVID: "Regis Philbin." (Laughter from the group.)
FACILITATOR: "O.K. but for this tape we are going to call you..."
DAVID: "Kathy Lee Gifford." (Laughter)
FACILITATOR: "How about we call you David?"
DAVID: "How about Frank Gifford?"
FACILITATOR: "That's a good one. Is David O.K. for this one?"
DAVID: "NoNoNoNoNoNOOOOOOOO!" (Playfully)
FACILITATOR: "We've got a bunch of names we can call you. Why don't you pick somebody to go next?"

(The choice of who goes next allows for interaction between the members right at the beginning of the group.)

DAVID: (Points to Hollis: sitting next to him.)
HOLLIS: "Hollis."
FACILITATOR: "All right Hollis, Hollis- why don't you pick who goes next."
HOLLIS: "Catrina." (Hollis points to the co-facilitator.)
CATRINA: "My name is Catrina."
FACILITATOR: "O.K. Catrina. And Catrina why don't you pick who goes next?" (She points to Cindy).
CINDY: "My name is Cynthia"
FACILITATOR: "All right Cynthia. Cynthia why don't you pick who goes next?"
CINDY: (Cynthia points to Gretta)
GRETTA: "My name is Gretta."
FACILITATOR: "All right Gretta. You guys are doing great. Gretta why don't you pick who goes next?"
GRETTA: (Gretta points to Leah)
LEAH: "My name's Leah."
FACILITATOR: "Leah. You look happy about that. You look happy about being here tonight. And Leah why don't you pick who goes next?"
LEAH: (Leah pointing to Lenore.) "Lenore."
LENORE: (Lenore is slumped over to her right side in the chair. She seems resistant to take part in the group.)

FACILITATOR: "Can you say your first name for us?"
LENORE: (Shakes head back and forth vigorously to indicate "no".)
FACILITATOR: "Is it O.K. for us to call you Lenore?"
LENORE: (No response)
FACILITATOR: (Trying to develop a rapport.) "Is there An 'A' at the end of that?"
LENORE: "Sometimes."
FACILITATOR: (Light laughing) "Sometimes?"
CINDY: "She doesn't like her middle name."
LENORE: "Don't you dare!!!!!!!!!!!!!!!!!!!!!"
(Group laughing)
FACILITATOR: "So we won't be talking about the middle name. So let's see what other people have heard about this. It's a chance to get into the movies. A chance to have counseling. What do other people think about the group? What do you think this is about? What do you think we will do here?"
HOLLIS: "Talk."
FACILITATOR: "Talk. Good Hollis!"
LENORE: "I don't know. To meet people?"
FACILITATOR: "...and to meet people. Did someone hear what Lenore said?"
DAVID: "To meet people...but we know everybody!"

The orientation stage with cognitive networking continues until...

Stage Two. Warm-up and Sharing

(This begins the Warm-up and Sharing Stage. The members of the group have begun orienting towards one another through the Cognitive Networking. Each phrase or group of phrases by a member is echoed back to him/her by others as a way of strengthening the communication loop. Once oriented, members will tell a bit of their story. Usually folks will say what they have done during the week as a way of easing into the material. There are usually two layers of information during this stage. The first is something about the functional aspects of the week, information like what one did, what may have happened that was different, etc. The second asks the members if they have a problem to work on. This may be asked directly or may naturally evolve as a form of self-disclosure. The shift in a normal process of group will be from horizontal self-disclosure to vertical self-disclosure. From generally less threatening information (what one did during the week) to more emotionally sensitive material ("I am scared about having surgery"). Cognitive networking continues through-out all the stages.

FACILITATOR: "Yeah, you guys know everybody, you live together. Well, one of the things I thought we could do as we begin the group is talk about what we did during the week. That way we can get used to hearing what people are working on during the week."

GRETTA: "Like what?"
FACILITATOR: "You tell me. What kind of things Gretta?"
GRETTA: "With what?"
FACILITATOR: "What did you do during the week?"
GRETTA: "This week?"
FACILITATOR: "Yeah."
GRETTA: "Its only Tuesday!!!"
FACILITATOR: "Right ! Well how about last week?"
GRETTA: "That's better. Like what? Inside the residence?"
FACILITATOR: "Yeah inside the residence, at work."
GRETTA: " I went to work Tuesday. I didn't go Monday, I went to the doctor's. No I didn't go to work Tuesday, I started work on Wednesday again. Then I came back and had a case conference."
FACILITATOR: "O.K. let's hang on there a second. Who heard what Gretta just said?"

(It is O.K. and even necessary to stop someone from talking to see if they were heard. Most members will respect this type of direction because for many of them being heard is a new experience that they want to have continue.)

At this point the group continues to warm up by having each of the members say something about their week. Finally the group returns their attention to Gretta who explains that she is going in for an operation. This reflects a shift from horizontal Self-Disclosure towards Vertical self-disclosure as Gretta now discusses her deeper feelings.

GRETTA: "...On Thursday...after fifteen years, I'm having surgery. I never had surgery in the residence before."
FACILITATOR: "O.K."
GRETTA: "So...and Catrina knows about it because she was with me last week."
FACILITATOR: "O.K. So you're a little bit frightened about going in for some surgery."
GRETTA: ".... and also because I don't to...I like doing this thing. I like to be on tape! (Everyone laughs)...And I feel I have to go because I scheduled it already."

(Notice the depth of Gretta's sharing. As we enter the second part of Stage Two (warm-up and sharing) where there is greater emotional involvement. This allows for self-disclosure from others while moving the whole group towards the central feature of the IBT group, the Enactment Stage.)

This is one way a protagonist is chosen in a group. There are 3 ways:

1. The facilitator can choose the protagonist. The issue is concrete, the protagonist is ready and the group is interested. Gretta is an easy choice in

this example.

2. The protagonist can ask to work in the group and the group can agree.
3. The group can choose who works. A question like “Who do you think needs our help?” may prompt the members to select a person who needs the group’s attention.

Please note that to choose a protagonist without the support of the group is usually a mistake. The facilitator must be certain the group both understands and is in sympathy or at least tolerant with the protagonist.

Stage Three: The Enactment Stage (action methods are introduced)

FACILITATOR: “O.K. So you’re a little nervous.... I have a way we could work on this.”
CINDY: “How?”
FACILITATOR: “ (To Cindy) I know you want to help...and Gretta would you be willing (not would you like) to do this, to....I’ll show you how it works.”
GRETTA: “Yeah but.... I was going to say how is this going to help my problem?”
FACILITATOR: “Let’s see how it works. Because I want to hear more about your problem.”
GRETTA: “Why?...What are you a doctor?” (The group laughs.)
FACILITATOR: “I am a doctor as a matter of fact.” (Motion for Gretta to come out to bring her chair to the center.)
DAVID: “Doctor Ben Casey” (Everybody makes jokes about doctors from TV programs.)
FACILITATOR: “We’re going to do a different kind of role playing than you’ve probably done before. What I am going to do is ask people to think about what Gretta said about going into the hospital. Right. Now the spot right behind Gretta here is where you would stand and you would say how you think she feels about going into the hospital.” As an example, right, I’m going to say: “I feel scared.” (Then turning to see Gretta’s face.) “Does that sound right?”
GRETTA: “Yes.”
FACILITATOR: “...and when I do that, when I stand here you know what they call this spot?”
GRETTA: “Role-playing.”
FACILITATOR: “Right...But they call this spot the double.”
(Everyone repeats the phrase “The Double.”)
DAVID: “Yeah that means you’re going to stand in for her...”
FACILITATOR: “ Yeah!!!!!...”
DAVID: “...on the operating table!!!!!!!!!!!!!!!!!!!”
FACILITATOR: “Well not on the operation!.... and since Cindy knows you so well, Cindy, why don’t you stand behind her here? (Gretta is seated in a chair in the middle of the group.)”O.K., I’ll put your pocketbook down here. (Cindy is standing behind the chair Gretta is seated in.) “Now Cindy is in the “double” role. Say how you think Gretta feels. Say I feel...”

CINDY: "errrrr...Gretta how do you feel?"
FACILITATOR: "...now you say how you THINK she feels."
CINDY: "Well she's...I know she's scared about having surgery done."
FACILITATOR: "O.K. so say now I'm scared."
GRETTA: "Who me?"

(Discuss confusion.)

FACILITATOR: "...because you're trying to be her feelings...You just try and take it in Gretta, you just wait there. (Now I direct my words toward Cindy) "Say I'm scared."
CINDY: "I'm scared."
FACILITATOR: "Does that sound right Gretta?"
GRETTA: "Yes it does."
FACILITATOR: "O.K. Cindy say some more-but say it as though you are Gretta."
CINDY: "I'm scared."
FACILITATOR: "...AND...."
CINDY: ".... about having the surgery done."
FACILITATOR: "O.K. does that sound right Gretta?"
GRETTA: "Yes."
FACILITATOR: "All right! Let's give Cindy a hand! Wasn't that great?"
(The group applauds)
FACILITATOR: " Cindy you did a good job. (She returns to her seat) Now Cindy did a good job of that, Lenore, how about you?"

(This is the introduction of the multiple double.)

LENORE: "I can't get up. I have a bad back."

(It is always an <u>invitation</u> to participate. Members must know that they are free to participate or not. Rather than see their lack of participation as resistance it may be more fruitful to think of it as a need for a different warm-up to action.)

FACILITATOR: "O.K., Dave how about you?"
LENORE: "David!"
DAVID: (As he is getting up to go stand behind Gretta's chair which is still in the middle of the group.) "Not David...Regis!"
FACILITATOR: "Regis...Regis!" (Now David is standing behind Gretta). "Say I feel..."
DAVID: "I feel..."
FACILITATOR: "How do you think she feels?"
DAVID: (In a very high pitched voice.) "I feel beautiful!"
FACILITATOR: "Yes she feel beautiful and how do you think she feels about the operation?"
DAVID: (Loving the attention) "Happy?"
(A number of group members say David's name with a note of admonishment

for not doing it the right way.)
DAVID: "Nervous. I feel nervous."
CINDY: "Scared."
FACILITATOR "Very good...and good Cindy that you said that. Let's give David a hand. All right, excellent." (Members applaud) "So it was good people know a little bit about how you feel. Who else wants to try? Leah how about you?"
LEAH: "You want me up there?"
FACILITATOR: "Yeah how about we give it a try."
(David: has returned to his seat and Leah makes her way to the space behind Gretta's chair.)
FACILITATOR : "That's very good. O.K." (Helping Leah into the spot.) "...and now as you're here say I feel."
LEAH: (Looking to see Gretta's face.) "How do you feel?"
FACILITATOR: "Now how do you think she feels?"
LEAH: (Repeating her question to Gretta.) "How do you feel?"
GRETTA: "Nervous."
FACILITATOR: (To Leah.) "What are you going to say?"
CINDY: "Scared."
LEAH: "Scared."
FACILITATOR: "She said, "I feel...nervous."
LEAH: "I feel nervous."
FACILITATOR: "...and scared."
LEAH: "...and scared."
GRETTA: "and I feel scared!!!!!!"
FACILITATOR: " O.K., good. All right, let's give Leah a hand, all right."

(Everyone claps and is quite happy with themselves. Gretta brings her chair back into the group. Now begins affirmation of the protagonist. This happens at the end of the enactment stage and just before the affirmation stage. It is sometimes referred to as the "post - encounter affirmation".)

FACILITATOR: " Let's give Gretta a hand for doing that. Let's give her a hand for coming out. That was terrific." (Everyone claps.) "What was good about what Gretta just did? What was good about what she just did? What did you like about it?"
DAVID: "She brought all of her emotions out." **(This is from the same man who has been so oppositional in the group!)**
FACILITATOR: "Yes David. That's very good. Cindy, what was good about what Gretta did? Because David said it was good she got her emotion out? What was good?"
CINDY: "It's good she brought her feelings out."
FACILITATOR: "Yes Cindy, good. Leah, how about you? What did you like about what Gretta did?"
LEAH: "She walked out...(Pointing to the center of the group.)
FACILITATOR: "Yes."

GRETTA: "I didn't walk out."
FACILITATOR: "Well (to Gretta) you walked out to the middle."
GRETTA: "Oh. Oh. Sorry."
FACILITATOR: (To Leah) "Right."
LENORE: "Yeah."
FACILITATOR: "That was good. O.K., and you liked that part that she took a little space for herself."
LEAH: "Yeah."
FACILITATOR: "Very good. Lenore what did you like about it?"
LENORE: "She was honest."
FACILITATOR: "Yes. She was honest. Lenore, very good! And Hollis, how about you? What did you like about what Gretta did?"
HOLLIS: "It's all right."
FACILITATOR: "It's all right. She did good, huh?"

Stage Four. The Affirmation Stage.

The facilitator begins to identify those factors reflected by members' participation.

FACILITATOR: "I think you did splendid today Gretta. You know because it takes a lot of courage to talk about that kind of feeling. And I think you did a terrific job with that. A really terrific job. How was it to have everybody say how you felt?"
GRETTA: "All right. But not next week, but on the twelfth I won't be here. When I do go I'll be out only a week. I got to lay in bed. Even though I miss the whole week, right, I can come back."
FACILITATOR: "You sure can. What do you say we give Gretta a hand for being so courageous." (The group applauds.)
CINDY: "But now I am going to ask you..."
FACILITATOR: "Well, Cindy. Cindy, I need to interrupt you because it's time for us to kind of wrap it up and that's an important question and you can ask Gretta that maybe when the group is over, but what I need to say is I really like to today say how you were really helping everybody. I noticed how you were helping Gretta. That you were helping Hollis. That you helped a lot of people in the group today and it was really clear because I think that that is something that you work on. You work on helping people."
CINDY: "Yes."
FACILITATOR: "So let's give Cindy a hand. I think that that was terrific." (The group applauds)

(The Affirmation Stage is an opportunity to try and reinforce interactive behaviors of the participants. This can be done by noticing the therapeutic factors that were displayed during the group. With Cindy, I am acknowledging "altruism", with Gretta it was her "self-disclosure" "installation of hope" and "acceptance/cohesion" which were reinforced.)

FACILITATOR: "Hollis, today you were working on your memory. And I noticed today that when you were trying to remember what people said, that as soon as people gave you a clue and helped you out a little bit, that you did a terrific job with that and that you said it back to them and told them just how you were feeling. So let's give Hollis a hand. Right! For today."
(The group applauds)
(This is reinforcing "guidance"[from others] and "self-understanding" for Hollis.)

FACILITATOR: " And David."
DAVID: "Regis, Regis!!!!!!"
FACILITATOR "Regis, Regis, Regis. You know what I liked? You know what I liked? Today you made us laugh, which was really great, that's a special gift, and you really made us laugh today. And yet when it was time to be serious you knew that Gretta was really being honest and sharing her feelings and you were able to tell her that. And I think that you did a great job because you knew when it was time to be funny and knew when it was time to be serious. So let's give, who should we call you, DAVID /Regis...."
(The group applauds)
(This reinforces David's "interpersonal learning".)

Please note the other members of the group were affirmed as the group came to a close.

In conclusion, group counseling for people with mental retardation is a methodology whose time has come. The need and desire for a therapeutic format where learning can occur is present. There is a need for peer support groups, with or without a particular curriculum attached to them. There is also the need for counseling groups designed for its members to not only change their behaviors, but feel different and better about themselves. More clinicians are willing to develop the necessary skills, and the participants are desirous of the kind of peer support only found through the group process.

References

Blatner, A. (1996). *Acting-in* (2nd Ed.), New York: Springer.

Blatner, A. (1988). *Foundations of psychodrama history, theory & practice*. New York: Springer.

Bloch, S., & Crouch E. (1985). *Therapeutic Factors in Group Psychotherapy*. New York: Oxford University Press.

Fletcher, R. (1984). Group therapy with mentally retarded persons with emotional disorders. *Psychiatric Aspects of Mental Retardation Reviews, 3*, 21-24.

Hingsburger, D. (1987). Sex counseling with the developmentally handicapped: The assessment and management of seven critical problems. *Psychiatric Aspects of Mental Retardation Reviews, 6*, 41-46.

Hurley, A.D. (1989). Individual Psychotherapy with mentally retarded individuals: A review and call for research. *Research in Developmental Disabilities, 10*, 261-275.

Hurley, A.D., & Hurley, F.J. (1988). Counseling and psychotherapy with mentally retarded clients: II. Establishing a relationship. *Psychiatric Aspects of Mental Retardation Reviews, 6*, 15-20.

Hurley, A.D., & Hurley, F.J.(1986). Counseling and psychotherapy with mentally retarded clients: I. The initial interview. *Psychiatric Aspects of Mental Retardation Reviews, 5*, 22-26.

Hurley, A, Pfadt A., Tomasulo D., & Gardner W. (1996). Counseling and psychotherapy. In J. Jacobson & J. Mulick (Eds.), *Manual of diagnosis and professional practice in mental retardation*. Washington, DC: American Psychological Association.

Keller, E. (1995). *Process and outcomes in interactive-behavioral groups with adults who have both mental illness and mental retardation*. Unpublished doctoral dissertation. Long Island University, C.W. Post Campus.

Pfadt, A. (1991). Group psychotherapy with mentally retarded adults: Issues related to design, implementation and evaluation. *Research in Developmental Disabilities, 12,* 261-285.

Razza, N., & Tomasulo, D. (1996a). The sexual abuse continuum: Therapeutic interventions with individuals with mental *retardation. The Habilitative Mental Healthcare Newsletter, 15,* 19-22.

Razza, N. & Tomasulo D. (1996b). The sexual abuse continuum: Part 2. Therapeutic interventions with individuals with mental *retardation. The Habilitative Mental Healthcare Newsletter, 15,* 84-86.

Razza, N., & Tomasulo, D. (1996c). The sexual abuse continuum: Part 3. Therapeutic interventions with individuals with mental retardation. *The Habilitative Mental Healthcare Newsletter, 15,* 116-119.

Steinberg, P., & Garcia A. (1989). *Sociodrama: Who's in your shoes*. New York: Praeger.

Tomasulo, D. (1998). *Action methods in group psychotherapy:Practical aspect.* Philadelphia: Accelerated Development: Taylor & Francis.

Tomasulo, D. (1994). Action techniques in group counseling: The double. *The Habilitative Mental Healthcare Newsletter, 13,* 41-45.

Tomasulo, D. (1992). *Interactive-behavioral group counseling for people with mild to moderate mental retardation*.(Two videos) New York: Young Adult Institute.

Tomasulo, D., Keller, E., & Pfadt A. (1995). The healing crowd. *The Habilitative Mental Healthcare Newsletter, 14,* 43-50.

Yalom, I. (1995). *Group psychotherapy* (4th ed). New York: Basic Books.

CHAPTER FIVE

THE EGOCENTRIC ERROR

Mary Ann Blotzer, L.C.S.W.-C.

Although our training emphasizes the importance of staying empathetically connected to the phenomenological world of our client, each of us brings an inevitable egocentricity to this endeavor. We remind ourselves that our gender, ethnicity and culture influence both our experiences and our interpretations of events. We remain open to the possibility that our clients may give vastly different interpretations to even those experiences that we hold in common.

By keeping this awareness conscious and by asking our clients about their lives, we are able to enter their phenomenological world. Only by entering this world can the transformative potential of therapy be realized; but this process becomes more complicated when we treat individuals with mental retardation. Neither our own experience nor our training really prepares us to adequately understand individuals who, by virtue of diminished intellectual function, may order their experience in a fashion vastly different from our own.

This chapter examines the impact that diminished intellectual functioning can have on the development of ego functions and object relations. Understanding these implications enables us to reconsider behavior that we formerly labeled as psychotic or as symptomatic of personality disorder. Armed with a deeper understanding of the client's psychic organization, we can develop formulations and descriptions that increase our empathetic understanding of the client and direct us to interventions that stimulate the growth of ego functions and object relations.

Despite our best efforts at empathy, we can never precisely know what another individual is feeling and thinking. We can listen carefully and strive for empathic attunement, but we bring an inevitable egocentricity to the process. This egocentricity of our own experience is shaped by gender, culture and even our own neurology. The sociolinguist, Deborah Tannen, has written about the difficulties that ensue when we assume that the opposite gender communicates as we do. Unlike beauty, meaning is not just in the eyes of the beholder. Gender can deafen us to meaning of the sender. Even greater deafening occurs when models based upon male experience are applied to females. Nearly a generation ago, Gilligan (1982) and Miller (1986) opened our eyes to the devaluation and misunderstanding that occurs when research findings based on men are inappropriately extended to women. When male developmental patterns are viewed as the sole norm, then the differing patterns of women are as less then ideal or as pathological. Similarly, the multicultural movement in counseling is an effort to move beyond the constraints of our culture-bound experiences and to consider fundamentally different outlooks. Without the awareness that there are different ways of being in the world (such as those that value connection more than autonomy), we risk pathologizing that which is different.

Our training as psychotherapists teaches us to pay close attention to the client's subjective experience. We know that therapy can only proceed when we accurately grasp the client's phenomenological world and empathetically convey this grasp to our client. Much of our work in therapy involves helping clients re-examine their beliefs and feelings. We attempt to ask the questions that stimulate clients to reflect upon their experiences and to consider alternative perspectives that can lead to a way out of their difficulties. It is precisely our empathetic, nonjudgmental grasp of how it is <u>now</u> for our clients that enables them to consider a transformation of that "now" to a better future.

With any client, we struggle to listen without preconceived notions so that we can be truly open to understanding how life is for that client. We struggle to balance empathy with interpretation (Josephs, 1995), and we struggle to address any damage to the therapeutic relationship that occurs from our inevitable mistakes. We do these things best when we have a good understanding of our client's character, defensive structure, and culture. Professional training programs increasingly emphasize the importance of understanding factors such as culture and gender; yet, where do we learn about the fundamentally different experiences of individuals with autism? Where do we learn about the implications that mental retardation can have upon ego development and object relations? We make an egocentric error when we assume that other individuals process sensory stimulation as we do, or that they have similar psychic structures for organizing their experience. Similarly, many of our formulations, such as our traditional view of psychosis, may not apply in the same way to persons with limited intellectual functioning. Many of the therapists who see individuals with mental retardation acknowledge the difficulty of applying some of the DSM IV categories to these clients. At best, many of the formulations that we apply to non-disabled persons may simply be unhelpful when applied to persons with mental retardation. Or, at worst, those notions may actually impede our understanding and effectiveness.

When evaluating or developing formulations, I am biased in favor of those that deepen our empathetic understanding of the client's world and guide us to interventions that stimulate the client's growth. And similar to the feminist perspective in psychotherapy, I look for differences in development and consider these from a standpoint of neutrality. This neutral stance enables me to think about phenomenon in a more dynamic fashion, and makes me less likely to pathologize that which is different.

In the following pages, I shall attempt to illustrate this approach that carefully considers how a given individual's mental retardation affects his or her ability to make sense of the world; and using this understanding, develop formulations that either stimulate growth or provide "prosthetic mental functions" (a concept to be covered later). Why is this important? The following passage illustrates the harm inflicted by well-intended but unattuned individuals who made the egocentric error of assuming that a child with autism experienced sensory stimulation as they did. This excerpt is from a book by Williams (1994) that provides front line dispatches from the world of autism:

"Entering the infant room, I saw a little girl about four years old curled up in the dark interior of a crate . . . Hung inside the crate were various mobiles and objects. The two supervising staff were excited by the novelty of their ideas and the equipment for the little girl. Like over enthusiastic relatives on their first meeting with a newborn, they were half inside the tiny crate with her. I stood there feeling ill as they bombarded her personal space with their bodies, their breath, their movement and their noise. Almost manically, they shook rattles and jiggled things in front of the girl as though they were a pair of overzealous witch doctors hoping to break the evil spell of autism.....I got the feeling that if they could have used a tire jack to pry open her soul and pour "the world" in, they would have done so and would never had noticed that their patient had died on the operating table. The little girl screamed and kicked, her arms up against her ears to keep their noise out and her eyes crossed to block out the bombardment of visual noise. I watched these people and wished they knew what sensory hell was. I was watching a torture where the victim had no ability to fight back in any comprehensible language. I stood almost numb with shock. She had no words to put to what was happening, to analyze or adjust to it as they did... It was medieval. These people had been told to use something that might work but no one had told them why or how... They were surgeons operating with garden tools and no anesthetic." (pp. 24-25).

The staff described here were trying to be helpful, yet without knowing it, they were inflicting torture. This provides us with an important lesson. Our task as therapists is more complicated when it comes to individuals with developmental disabilities. We need to understand more than just their thoughts and feelings. We need to understand how they take in and organize their experience, how they integrate and organize data from their senses, which senses are under- or over- reactive and to which kinds of stimulation, how their cognitive structures work and how they understand time and causality. Through considering these aspects and thinking about them in sufficiently disciplined and thorough ways, behavior that previously seemed incomprehensible and deviant becomes understandable and even adaptive. We can then develop appropriate interventions.

What follows are some beginning attempts to answer these questions. These attempts are often imperfect and inadequate. Whenever I write and think about these issues, I am aware of the tremendous gaps in my knowledge and understanding. Hence, this is not a "how to" chapter, but one which I hope will stimulate greater thinking and discussion.

"They Keep Hitting Me"

Karen, a 25-year-old Euro-American woman, tells me that her co-workers hit her. She describes her job in a segregated program as a place where everyone is mean to her and where she is frequently hit. It soon becomes apparent from listening to her and checking out the situation, that what she tells me cannot possibly be true. I could describe her as paranoid, as delusional, or as telling stories, but none of these descriptions would be fair to her, nor do they deepen our understanding of her. Karen is talking about how she feels at work. Karen's internal world, the world of feelings and images, is chaotic. Because of the limited symbolic capacity associated with her mental retardation, she manages her internal world by concretely projecting it onto the outside world. With limited skills for managing her intense feelings and limited symbolic capacity, she externalizes her inner reality. She tells me that people at work hit her, because she lacks both the internal psychic organization and linguistic skills to tell me about her inner world.

Karen feels disliked by her coworkers, so she tells me that they hit her. We can also consider that some of her own rage is projected onto her co-workers. The important issues for therapy are to stay connected to Karen's feeling that work is a hostile place and to help her make the distinction between how things feel inside and how they actually are in the external world. The false statements she makes about the external world reflect primitive mental organization, stunted both by trauma and intellectual disability (rather than an underlying thought disorder that requires psychotropic medication). Understanding her statements in this way increases our dynamic understanding of her and guides us towards intervention that can stimulate her growth.

A less extreme example of a patient managing his internal feelings by making concrete but false statements about external events comes from Steve, a 40 year old man with autism and mild mental retardation. I have seen Steve for many years, and he has made many gains; but at some point we came to a period where the therapy felt a bit flat because there were no pressing external issues. Steve used this time to check in with me and to tell me about the important events in his life - those centered on his visits with his family, on whether the van arrived on time, and which counselor was leaving. One day Steve announced that his long time house-counselor, Jim, was going to be fired. Steve is a great source of information about agency personnel matters, and has been unfailingly accurate, much to the dismay of the agency's management, who often want to delay announcements or keep certain matters confidential. Steve always knew what was happening, even when he wasn't supposed to. There was something about Steve's announcement that didn't seem right to me, so I began to delve into the matter more. Within the next few minutes of exploring this "news flash," Steve acknowledged that he wanted Jim fired because Jim had kept him out too late the previous evening, despite Steve's repeated urging to go home. Unlike Karen, Steve was able to readily acknowledge that Jim was not going to be fired. Rather, Steve was so angry that he wished for Jim's firing, but was unable to generate this distinction on his own. The stress of his anger caused him to regress to a more primitive position.

This view reflects my bias in favor of formulations that increase our dynamic understanding of the patient and lead to deeper inquiry. Viewing Karen in this way leads to more productive treatment goals, such as helping her to distinguish between how relationships feel inside her, and what real people do in the external world. With Steve, we were able to talk about feeling angry enough to wish that Jim would be fired, and to distinguish this from the actual reality.

"Don't Say That": The Separation Between Thinking and Doing

So much of therapy is about thinking and about creating a space for thinking. In this space for thinking, we can contemplate actions, talk about what we feel like doing and reflect on the possible consequences. But, sometimes we see patients for whom thinking and talking about certain ideas is frightening because they do not firmly hold the distinction between thinking and doing.

Susan, a 15 year old Euro-American, was referred because of her long history of severe aggressive outbursts. Susan has a complex profile of neuropsychological deficits, including sensory difficulties consistent with pervasive developmental disorder. She meets the diagnostic criteria for mild mental retardation as well as for other developmental disabilities and mental disorders. Her ability to separate thinking from doing is not firmly established. When she is at her best (rested, gratified, and unstressed by external demands), she will tell me about the things that make her mad and the impulses that she feels, and we gently explore these. Susan's equilibrium is easily disrupted, a characteristic consistent with her PDD. At these times, she loses the space for thinking. The following excerpt conveys something of this:

> Susan: I want to go home. I'm tired. I want my mother. No, I'm not tired. I'm having a good day.
> Me: It sounds as though you are struggling.
> Susan: No. Don't say that. I'm having a good day.

My choice of the word "struggling" was inaccurate and inappropriate. It was probably too loaded for her and too associated with aggression. "A good day" is Susan's term for a day without aggression, and my suggestion that she was struggling to maintain an even keel was too threatening to her. It threatened to overwhelm her already shaky equilibrium because she had lost the space for thinking, as well as the separation between thinking and doing. Thinking about her troubling feelings threatened to overwhelm her and move her into action. I quickly reassured her that, indeed, she was having a good day, and shifted into efforts to help her restore her equilibrium. Later in the session she returned to her contradictory feelings:

Susan: I want to go back to Evergreen (the school that she was expelled from). I like Forest View (her current school) better.
Me: You have two feelings.
Susan: No, stop it.

Susan also has very limited capacity to bear her ambivalent, conflicting feelings and to think about and discuss these. The pressure of her feelings threatens to overwhelm her, and she becomes very irritable and brittle. At these times, she needs me to help her maintain her calm by talking about these issues in a way that helps her to manage them. My goal is to lend her the structures and concepts that will enable her to manage her feelings. Susan's therapy needs to be more supportive and less dynamic. Instead of noting that she has two feelings, I should have made a more structured comment.

This issue also intersects with the difficulties many of our clients have at regulating and soothing themselves. They often feel out of sorts both physiologically and psychologically. As therapists, we need to recognize this sensory, physiological aspect to our client's difficulties and address it. We need to arrange our office environment and even adjust our style to minimize the risks of overwhelming individuals with sensory difficulties. I have patients, for example, who find eye contact stressful, so I tend to look away when speaking with them. One of my patients is easily disturbed by loud noises and even a normal speaking volume is sometimes too much for him. I keep the overhead florescent lights off in my office and use regular lamps when seeing individuals with visual sensitivities.

Prosthetic Mental Functions

Mental retardation is such a broad concept that we sometimes lose sight of its functional implications for a given individual. Teasing out these implications can be tremendously useful in understanding the nature of a client's difficulty. Many individuals with mental retardation lack the cognitive constructs that enable them to make sense of the world in the same way that we do. (Try getting a coherent history from a client whose sense of time is not firmly established). The distant past may be merged with the recent past; moreover, past, present and future may not be firmly established.

Some clients with mental retardation may have difficulty with themes of change and transformation because they remain in a stage of preoperational thinking. They become "stuck" when trying to process certain changes because of their cognitive deficits. I find it enormously useful to consider what aspect of a client's difficulties are due to more or less enduring deficits and how to address this. "Deficit" is a loaded term in the developmental disabilities field, but I believe that it is necessary to recognize the substantial and enduring limits that some of our clients face. Doing so enhances our understanding of the challenges they face and helps us formulate realistic goals. Sometimes what we offer to our clients are prosthetic mental functions - strategies that we lend them to help them cope with situations that they are inadequately equipped for.

In a previous book (Blotzer & Ruth, 1995), I described the case of Alma, who was described as being "obsessed with death." Alma's frequent questions about individuals who had died were not fueled by a macabre fascination with death, but were simply the results of her underdeveloped cognitive structures attempting to process loss and transformation. When Alma would bring up the names of individuals who had died, her mother (a gifted and sensitive parent) would respond by saying, "You're remembering (name)." Alma would latch onto this phrase and we could talk about <u>thinking about</u> individuals who were no longer present. Like a prosthesis, Alma's use of, "you're remembering," was a bit awkward, but it helped her to manage an experience that she had insufficient resources of her own to cope with. We frequently metabolize complicated or affect-laden experiences for our patients and reflect these back to them in a more understandable fashion. We lend our ego and ego functions, as well as cognitive structures, to our patients to help them manage both their own internal worlds and external reality.

On Demand vs. Scheduled Feeding

I have a patient, Cora, the depths of whose egocentricity can take my breath away. She leaves a trail of enraged supervisors and house-counselors in her wake because of her insensitive, demanding and sometimes incessant interactions with them. Like an infant, she wants what she wants when she wants it. Her inability to manage strong feeling states, waiting, and uncertainty lead her to become so overwhelmed, disorganized and agitated that she will go to almost any length to get her needs met. She will awaken staff in the middle of the night, phone the same person 20 times in a row, and even call the police to come to her house to help her find something.

As insensitive as her behavior can be, I often feel sympathy and sometimes even admiration for Cora. Although I don't like it when she calls me repeatedly, and I have set certain limits with her (which she respects), I do recognize that at times she needs "on demand feeding." I have had to adapt the structure of her therapy to address this issue.

The traditional model of therapy - the patient coming for regularly scheduled appointments, usually for 50 minutes, one or more times each week - was developed for patients who had the internal capacity to mentally contain their life experiences and bring these to their regularly scheduled appointments. But many of our patients with mental retardation may be limited in their capacity to do this. Their lives may have a more tumultuous, moment-to-moment quality that makes it difficult for them to come to therapy several days after a key experience and talk this out. I've often thought that clinicians who work with these individuals need to spend more time discussing and writing about these difficulties. Do we need to be more flexible at setting additional appointments? Do we need to be more available for crisis phone calls? One patient of mine used to phone me several times each week during the early years of her therapy, and to my thinking, this was necessary. So much happened in her daily life to stir her up, and she had such limited resources for managing her internal life, that she needed to phone me on her own schedule. While this approach was unorthodox, I believe it was a necessary accommodation to her limits that enabled her to make more progress in therapy than would otherwise have been possible. Throughout this time, we would use her regularly scheduled therapy appointment to discuss what had led her to call and how she coped with those feelings. My goal was to help her develop the capacity for recognizing the impulsive moments when she felt compelled to call me, to help her understand her experience at these times, and to develop her own resources for managing these events.

Although I have occasionally reacted impatiently to Cora, we have maintained an effective alliance over many years. I think this is because I understand and accept her limits. We talk directly about her difficulty waiting and her persistence. I try to give her concrete strategies to manage the stress she feels when something in her life is unsettled. We also discuss the things she does that make people want to help her, and the things she does that push people away.

Even though she has infuriated some staff, there have also been those who patiently and helpfully stayed with her for one to two years. Invariably, these were individuals who accepted her interpersonal limits and her egocentricity. They did not take it personally, and they did not expect her to show much sensitivity or empathy. They accepted the limits of her personality development in much the same way that they accepted her intellectual limits. Both were neutral conditions for which they could make accommodations.

Structural Aspects of Therapy

Orthodox psychoanalytic therapy does not concern itself with the patient's external life. The patient is presumed competent to manage his or her life outside of therapy, and the analyst is only concerned with what the patient brings to treatment. Because most of the contemporary approaches to therapy have some roots in the psychoanalytic approach, vestiges of traditional analytic structure and assumptions persist throughout much of the "how" of therapy. Sometimes this structure is appropriate, and the assumptions warranted, but I believe that we must reexamine these to determine if these meet the needs of all of our patients. What follows is a beginning examination of some of these components. My purpose in doing so is to stimulate greater thinking and writing on these issues, so that we mindfully choose approaches that best serve a given patient.

Traditional approaches assume that a patient can adequately and accurately (other than through the influence of psychosis or defensive distortion) discuss life events with his or her therapist; yet, many individuals with cognitive disabilities are unable to do so. They may not be able to provide an accurate chronology, for example, because their sense of time is distorted due to their cognitive limitations. The cognitive, linguistic, and sensory disabilities that are associated with mental retardation can alter the patients' life experiences and can limit their ability to discuss their lives. Although skillful, experienced therapists can often work effectively in these circumstances; targeted work around a focal issue is often difficult. In these circumstances, the effectiveness of therapy can be enhanced by involving others. Perhaps the house-counselor or parent needs to call before sessions or participate in some sessions to provide important information. The decision to do so must be balanced with concern for the therapeutic alliance.

Sometimes the therapist needs to be actively involved in the patient's external life. While I have never gone to the job site of a nondisabled client, I have visited the job sites and interviewed the supervisors of some of my clients with mental retardation. Such involvement, when warranted, has usually been invaluable at understanding and resolving work difficulties, and clients have felt supported rather than threatened by my involvement with their supervisors. Many therapists are reluctant to involve themselves in these ways because it goes against their training, and they worry that such involvement will impede their client's therapy. Although this is a possibility, we cannot afford to reflexively reject such involvement. We must consider the client's needs and whether we need to make accommodations in "the way things are done" in order to better meet the client's needs.

Countertransference Issues

As therapists, our training has taught us that our reactions to patients are powerful clues. Indeed, therapy is not just about what is said, but also about what is felt. Being with client evokes feelings, and it is our job to sort out what the patient before us is evoking in us and why. Sometimes the patient before us is in deep despair, and this despair may feel so hard for *us* to bear that we try to finesse the pain away with some superficial pabulum. Unfortunately, this response from us communicates that the patient's pain is intolerable even to the therapist, leaving him or her feeling even more alone. Other times we feel an intense anger rise in us while our patient appears calm, and we need to consider that this anger is the patient's disowned anger projected into us. At times we may feel boredom, and this is usually a sign that we are with a patient who is disconnected from his/her feelings. These feelings are often intense and require our professionalism to manage appropriately, but we can usually share these easily with colleagues and in supervision, know that these are part of each therapist's professional experience.

Acknowledging our reactions towards patients, using these productively in the therapy, and discussing these with colleagues, can be more complicated when our clients have intellectual disabilities. Reactions to clients are always an intersection between the therapist's own history and the client's dynamics; and clients with mental retardation present added issues for therapist to grapple with. The following list of issues is not meant to be exhaustive, but to open this area up for further exploration.

Encounters With "Retardedness"

Mental retardation evokes strong reactions and defenses against these reactions. Sometimes we are repulsed by a client's appearance, mannerisms, or poor hygiene. Sometimes we see individuals whose needs and drives are unmodulated, unfiltered, and totally "out there."

Mental retardation can bring us face to face with what feels most damaged and awkward in ourselves, and somewhere between the extreme reactions of repulsion and condescension lies the space for forming authentic relationships. Therapists who take this work seriously go through a process of coming to terms with retardation. Many individuals find it difficult to acknowledge their less than positive reactions to clients with mental retardation, and they may need support from their supervisors. Asking whether aspects of the client make the trainee uncomfortable can sometimes free up the trainee to explore this. Others may initially attempt to defend against some of the uncomfortable realities of mental retardation by viewing clients too positively or protectively.

It is a natural human tendency to try to "freeze frame" complicated or painful realities. Because it is difficult to hold all the facets together, we reduce ambiguity or discomfort by trying to squeeze out that which is too painful. Hence, we hear comments such as, "individuals with Down Syndrome are so loving," or we see the media's fascination with "super crips" - individuals with disabilities who do it all. By focusing on these images, we attempt to banish painful realities, for example, that many individuals with mental retardation lead marginalized lives, and that some are miserably unhappy.

Therapists are not immune to these tendencies. We eagerly look for images that corroborate with our sense of how we want things to be because confronting the complete picture is too disquieting (perhaps because we are shaken out of our complacency, or because the client stirs up our feelings about the weak and vulnerable parts of ourselves).

Our efforts to stay empathetically attuned to clients with mental retardation can sometimes leave us feeling retarded; we feel stuck, or slow, or befuddled. This can be a good thing, for this can be the starting point for an effective connection with our client. It can mean that we have found the right pace. We need to know something of how it feels to be retarded - something of the awkwardness and frustration. Only by understanding and metabolizing this, can we begin to connect authentically with our patients.

Feelings of Boredom

Boredom is usually, but not always, a sign that we are with a patient who is disconnected from her feelings. Although this can be the case with patients who have mental retardation, therapists sometimes feel boredom for other reasons. Entire stretches of therapy can feel boring and sterile, as though nothing meaningful is going on. The therapy feels stalled or hopeless. The therapist begins to think about termination, believing that he or she has nothing more to offer the patient. But jumping to this conclusion, although it helps the therapist escape an uncomfortable situation, may shortchange the patient.

At times we feel this "something" is more complicated than boredom. Perhaps it is the depletion that can result from working with a very primitive client. I went through a period in my work with Karen, the woman cited earlier in this chapter, that left me feeling exhausted. For several sessions, Karen was quite consumed by her rage at her house counselor. The house counselor told Karen that she needed to bathe everyday, and Karen could barely contain her hurt and anger. She talked about leaving the house and living on the street. A recovered alcoholic, she even talked about drinking again. All my attempts to get her to reflect upon why she felt so angry seemed futile.

I found myself feeling depleted and something more. The effort of staying empathetically connected to her was taxing, and I think that I also felt a unique brand of fatigue that represents unexpressed frustration. I didn't want her to be stuck in this primitive place. I wanted her to move beyond it and use her own limited ego strengths (or borrow some of mine) to create the distance from her rage that would enable her to reflect upon it, and transform it, rather than merely feeling it. She was, however, unable to respond to any of my attempts, and I felt frustrated at my inability to move her beyond her rage. As each of my efforts failed, I returned to empathy. This kept us connected but it came at a cost for me. Being this close to her primitive world made me uncomfortable. It wasn't a world that I wanted to visit, yet I knew that it was the world she lived in.

Interestingly, this empathy was somehow sufficient to contain her. Karen weathered this episode without resorting to the drinking, high-risk sexual activity and acts of aggression that had been her previous strategies. One week she simply walked in and announced that she was "over" being mad.

I must admit that I often felt inadequate and frustrated in my work with Karen. I thought about terminating, but I always knew that Karen was attempting to recreate her early object relations - notably, her abandonment by her mother.

When we feel a sustained period of boredom or frustration, we owe it to our patients to explore this in supervision so that we can develop fresh insights into the therapy. Sometimes we feel bored because the pace of change is so slow, or because staying connected to the client's pace - a key component of empathy - wears us out. Being with a stuck client, or a slow client is taxing. It takes an extra effort to stay connected, and this extra effort can deplete us. Perhaps our "boredom" or "fatigue" is a defense against "negative" feelings. Our responsibility to our client requires us to acknowledge our countertransferential reactions, to seek supervision so that we can develop a more complete understanding, and to make decisions on the future course of the therapy based upon this knowledge, rather than upon our desire to escape an uncomfortable situation.

Inconclusive Thoughts

Our training as psychotherapists is usually inadequate for the daunting task of working effectively with individuals with mental retardation. Effective therapy with these clients requires a comprehensive understanding of the implications that the individual's intellectual disabilities have upon his/her ego functioning and object relations. We need to know something about the client's hard wiring and sensory peculiarities, lest we unwillingly inflict sensory torture. Finally, we need to consider alterations to the traditional structure of therapy. Clients with mental retardation are typically less able to contain strong experiences and store these for examination in therapy.

We need new ways of examining our client's difficulties. Rather than labeling our clients as psychotic or borderline, we need to think more deeply about the nature of their difficulties. Psychotic or delusional thinking may reflect limited symbolic capacity. "Fixations" may simply stem from limited cognitive abilities in addition to their dynamic meaning. We can feel more empathetic toward clients with personality disorders when we view their level of character development in the same light as we view their intellectual development. The more precisely we are able to identify the source of a client's difficulty, the more likely we are to develop constructive intervention that can stimulate their growth.

References

Blotzer, M. A., & Ruth, R. (1995). *Sometimes you just want to feel like a human being: Case studies of empowering psychotherapy with people with disabilities*. Baltimore: Paul H. Brookes.

Gilligan, C. (1982). *In a different voice*. Cambridge: Harvard University Press.

Josephs, L. (1995). *Balancing empathy and interpretation*. Northvale, NJ: Jason Aronson.

Miller, J. B. (1986). *Toward a new psychology of women*. Boston: Beacon Press.

Williams, D. (1994). *Somebody somewhere*. New York: Random House.

CHAPTER SIX

THE INNER LIFE AND THE OUTER WORLD IN TREATING PERSONS WITH MENTAL RETARDATION: WORKING WITH PAUL

Richard Ruth, Ph.D.

Many people committed to mental health work of various kinds with people with mental retardation are rightly suspicious of psychoanalytic approaches. The more thoughtful of these suspicions are grounded in the correct observation that much of the phenomenology of mental retardation, and thus many of the subjective difficulties of people with mental retardation, are grounded in the impact of an unaccommodating and disempowering society. It seems well established by the past two generations' experience in the United States that when people with mental retardation move from impossible lives to more possible lives - from institutions to community settings, from lives of isolation to lives with support systems - their emotional well-being and behavioral functioning tend, on the whole, to improve.

However these sociopolitical observations may contextualize a clinical situation. They cannot offer much guidance for how to address the issues a specific person with mental retardation may bring to a mental health professional. What applies to a large group of people may or may not be applicable to a particular person; furthermore, clinicians seem to be meeting significant numbers of persons with mental retardation who have grown up within the current generation, who have had access to good special education, behavioral programming, and community-based services and supports, but who nevertheless have significant emotional distress.

Some of this may simply be attributable to the fact that psychological and psychiatric disorders occur in persons with mental retardation just as they do in the population at large. However, something beyond this may be involved. Many of these people have kind and supportive people in their lives but little real intimacy or satisfaction (Blotzer & Ruth, 1996). They may have jobs but little fulfillment through their work, places to live but little sense of real community, and more the possibility than the fulfillment of real self-direction. The absence of institutional options can create a terror of freedom, particularly in a social environment where resources may be scant and obstacles to full social inclusion remain ample. It is therefore perhaps not surprising that such persons - whose issues, in a slightly different context, are not very different from those of many young adults without mental retardation - might seek out therapists, and psychoanalytically oriented therapists at that.

How can a psychoanalytic approach work with problems that have their origin in the external world? An answer might begin with the observation that, from its very beginnings, Freud (1916-1917/1965) emphasized that many psychological difficulties begin with real, painful experiences in the world. Freud argued however that such experiences both crystallized as symptoms and became most accessible to therapeutic help when they were taken up in their representations in a person's inner life, as these emerged in the context of a therapeutic relationship.

He further argued, as do contemporary psychoanalytically oriented clinicians, that experiences are never internalized directly; rather, what people experience always differs from what they remember about it. Experiences pass through filters of affects, expectations, past history, beliefs, desires, conscious and unconscious fantasies, context and associations before they acquire their representation in the inner life, making for inevitable distortions. Developmental disability is not an obstacle to such a process Heinemann & De Groef, (1997); Ruth, (1995); and Sinason, (1992).

To the contrary, thinking that takes place between patient and therapist, in a clinical situation, about the distance and tension that exist between a lived experience and its inner representation can constitute a powerful mechanism for change. When the understanding of how experience is represented becomes dynamic - when the conflicts inherent in lived experience become articulated, and the thoughts, feelings and fantasies that get in the way of resolving them come alive then therapists are in a position to help leverage progress. This is so whether a therapist is working directly with a patient in a traditional therapy relationship, or is working with other persons in an indirect effort to be of help to a person with a developmental disability.

Sinason (1986) has demonstrated that the absence of high-level verbal expressive ability and the severity of a developmental disability need not be obstacles to the application of a psychoanalytically grounded approach. Perhaps more controversially, it can also be argued that, at least in some circumstances, this approach can be useful even when difficult external conditions in a person's life do not change.

There is actually a long history of psychoanalytic interest in work with persons with seriously disadvantaged lives. Altman (1995) has summarized and analyzed this history, and the reader is referred to his work for a fuller discussion. Shapiro (1997) and others have made a valuable contemporary contribution to this literature as well. Consistently, what clinicians in this tradition have emphasized is that it is precisely the delinking of inner reality from external circumstances that gives psychoanalytically oriented therapeutic work its potential impact. That is, the development, in therapy, of awareness of the subtle distortions that occur during the translation of external experience into psychic reality can help people see the ways that they add to their externally imposed burdens and unconsciously impose further constrictions on their subjective experience and behavioral repertoire. This insight can lead to a fuller, more creative way of responding to external circumstances, no matter how adverse these circumstances might be. The present paper will be an attempt to explore how this perspective may be able to contribute to deepening an understanding of the potential for psychoanalytic psychotherapy to be of help to severely disadvantaged persons with developmental disabilities.

Case Example

Clinical history. Paul is a 22-year-old, European-American man with moderate to mild mental retardation. He is tall and very thin and is missing some teeth, though he is not unattractive. He typically wears black jeans, inexpensive running shoes that he claims are a designer brand, and colorful T-shirts, often bearing images of a Tasmanian devil or some other aggressive cartoon character. Looking at him, it is hard to tell if he is weak or wiry. I have treated him in psychoanalytically oriented group therapy for four years.

Paul defines himself, with pride, as a redneck. He makes overtly racist comments, though he makes clear that these are not directed to me (I am Latin American) or another group member, who is Korean. To the contrary, he can be remarkably solicitous and kind to persons he knows who do not meet his stereotyped constructs of social acceptability. While he can become virulently enraged if someone says that his shoes are not really Nikes, his closest friend is an older man with chronic, treatment-refractory schizophrenia, who wears old, unfashionable clothes and is rarely competently groomed.

Paul is counted as a successful graduate of special education classes in a sophisticated public system. Like many such students, he teetered over the years between "educable" and "trainable" categories (no longer in use in the official nomenclature, but still robust in the corridors). He can write his name but not much else; read some single words, but not enough to understand a newspaper headline or a simple written text; and has some number concepts but cannot really count or calculate. He cannot make change from a dollar when he makes a simple purchase, for instance. What portion of the responsibility for his poor functional abilities is attributable to his organic limitations, what portion to failures of his educational experience, what portion to constraints on learning stemming from mental illness, and what portion to difficult family circumstances and social disadvantage is not clear.

In my contact with Paul, I have been impressed by how lacking he is in contact with his own desires, in particular a desire to master many skills and many processes in his external world. In that this retreat from mastery and from investing in his own desires seems to serve defensive functions, Paul seems to have substantial secondary mental handicap (Sinason, 1986), a psychodynamic process that exacerbates the impact of his retardation.

In school, beyond whatever academic skills he could assimilate, the staff tried to help Paul develop some type of conventional socialization and to teach him - largely by teachers accompanying him on job trials - skills for functioning in unskilled positions (cleaning jobs, for instance). In spite of years of effort by good people, Paul left school without good social or job skills.

After leaving school, Paul was transitioned, less clumsily than most, to a system of adult services. He lives at home with his parents (by his preference and theirs) and his work is arranged through a local agency that contracts with businesses that employ the labor of persons with developmental disabilities. Sometimes he works on a "crew" that travels together from job to job. With the crew, he has placed take-out menus from a pizza delivery service on doorknobs, helped clean an impressive variety of government agencies and private businesses, and worked on a truck farm. From time to time, he has also been tried out in more demanding and competitive settings, working with a one-to-one job coach. His vocational service providers are well trained, empathic, flexible, and highly creative.

Paul has not been one of their success stories, which is why he was eventually referred to me. Actually, he was first seen for several years by a very good psychiatrist, who tried him on a variety of medications with very limited results. Neither the vocational staff who initiated the visits to the psychiatrist nor the psychiatrist himself is at all hostile to psychotherapeutic approaches to helping people with developmental disabilities; but, in Paul's case, there seemed to be a consensus that he was too inaccessible to a therapeutic relationship for this to be a workable first approach.

Paul was referred for therapy as a last resort. His problems were several. On the job he was inattentive and frequently strayed off task, and it was extremely difficult for staff to get him focused back on work. With coworkers he was playful in a way that hovered on the border between playfulness and frank aggression. He would poke, tease, insult and throw things. He was often very provocative - sometimes in response to a perceived slight, sometimes in response to no apparent trigger. His attention span was very short and he demanded to be the center of attention. If staff were momentarily attending to the needs of someone else on the crew, Paul often took this as an intolerable slight and would sulk and pout. He was quick to anger, and to uncontrolled aggressive acts when angry. Some of these acts were rather dangerous, not so much because of intent to harm, but because of lack of awareness of the impact of his actions.

Paul has a powerful sense of grandiosity. He has told me he is a police officer, a firefighter, and in charge of security at a hospital. Even more troublesomely, to the vocational staff, he is fond of going around to businesses in the neighborhood of his jobs and telling employees he is from the police department or the fire department. The people he goes to are aware he is mentally retarded - Paul does not use these words, but his developmental disability is obvious to most people - and often just laugh him off or humor him.

Paul can challenge this attempt at accommodation (and even friendship of sorts), by being remarkably unrelenting in his efforts to tell these employees of local businesses what to do, and in taking up significant amounts of their time. At times, employees at businesses, females particularly, become afraid of Paul and panicky because they are unsure whether he represents a danger to them. Some of this seems to be the terror of our own unacceptable parts that many of us project onto persons with mental retardation, but some seems particular to Paul. He is always there, insistent, and becomes angry when people try to get back to their work.

Paul has no friendships outside of his job and the group, and few even in these restricted environments. The interaction between his powerful grandiosity and the underlying sense of unconfessable shame flowing from his limitations (which can give a particular, angry edge to his words and deeds) leads him to hold himself apart from others and alienate them if they try to get close to him. Paul thinks that he is better than everyone else and simultaneously unworthy of them.

Paul has one older brother, without developmental disabilities, who has led something of a marginal life - frequent low - level involvement's with the police, unstable relationships and work history, and likely alcoholic. More often than not, he lives in a crowded apartment with Paul and his parents.

Paul's mother works to support the household. On the surface, she is intensely interested in Paul, and in "helping" him; she has been enraged with me at times when I have declined to talk in detail about what he is doing in group. She shows very little understanding of Paul and has assimilated very little from what vocational staff, the psychiatrist or I have tried to tell her. She oscillates between treating Paul in a mean, angry way and treating him with a shallow kindness that confuses him, and which he experiences as erotically tinged. From Paul's descriptions in therapy of his experience of his mother, it is clear that he experiences her as intrusive, castrating, very needy, and lost, and that he senses she experiences him as more interesting and available than her husband, which terrifies Paul. However, Paul is able to maintain almost none of this in awareness. Insights flash and fade. He does not talk about his mother much. When he does say something, it is usually as if something has percolated up from his unconscious and temporarily pierced his defenses, and he is eager to expel the comment from awareness and discussion.

From my limited interactions with her, it has been my impression that having a son with a developmental disability has been a source of intense sadness and terror to Paul's mother. He has betrayed her dreams, though on another level he has sustained them - he accepts her flirtations, at least, which her husband does not. She feels helpless and confused, but this has felt too threatening for her to address openly, even with professionals who have met her with every openness and sympathy. To the contrary, she turns out her frustration and finds some solace in virulent racism. She was enraged when she called me once, got my answering machine, and heard that I spoke Spanish. For a long time, in a masterful application of a variable reinforcement scheme, she would bring Paul to therapy inconsistently - some weeks late, some not at all. Now he comes regularly and on time, but often enacts his mother's covert wishes by immediately wandering off and coming into group late.

Paul's father is physically disabled and an alcoholic, and he stays home most of the time watching television. Paul describes him (and I have experienced him) as a mean, angry man, always enraged when he emerges from his stupor, and in scant control of his behaviors. For example, once Paul called to say he would not be able to attend a session - a big achievement for Paul, who takes sadistic delight in being unpredictable and rarely doing what he should - and the father could be heard screaming and cursing in the background, berating and threatening Paul for telling "that man" – me - what was "none of his goddamn business." Paul longs for his father's attention, identifies with him (there is an emerging part of Paul that does not), and hates him so intensely that he can barely express it at all. I admire Paul for this restraint; it is one of his strengths and a source of ego capacity that hopefully, through treatment, can grow.

Paul says he has a girlfriend, a woman about his age with developmental disabilities, but that he sees her only every six months or so, when he runs into her on a job. He seems to know that a man his age is supposed to say he has a girlfriend and tries to carry this off, but his heart is not in it - nor are his hormones apparently. Paul has very low libidinal drives, does not masturbate, and shows little interest in sex or sexuality. Part of this seems to have to do with his parents' discouragement of any notion of Paul becoming involved with a woman, and with the covert shadow play he lives out with his mother. Part of this also seems to have to do with latent homosexuality. Paul loves to hang out with policemen, firemen, construction workers, and men who work in hardware stores. Like a preoedipal child, he will say, with all seriousness, that he *is* a policeman.

Paul has lived out his life at this preoedipal level of primativity. He confuses who he is with what he does, and rarely seems to have experienced that his efforts were rewarded or that his aspirations (even humble ones) were achieved. While he has a great vocational staff, they cannot make a life for him. One could think of him, in formal diagnostic terms, as having a reactive attachment disorder and a conduct disorder. One could also think of him as having grown up in an environment so inadequate that few could survive there.

Psychotherapy material and processes. How does all of this play out in group? And how has therapy tried to help Paul? A starting point was my assessment that there was no space in which to work with his parents. They did not seem able or willing to talk with me, or with a colleague, in an open, meaningful, honest manner. That is a painful assessment to make, and not one I make frequently or easily; yet, it was my grounded view of Paul's situation.

In group, Paul is himself, and I think any therapeutic leverage the process affords begins with the fact that there is space and time allowed for this. If nothing else, group, for Paul, is an encounter with the genuine. As mentioned earlier, Paul generally arrives late. He comes to the clinic on time, peeks around, talks to people in the waiting room, and then makes his rounds of the local businesses. Until she involved the police in making him stop, he would visit the sole attendant (female) at a veterinary hospital and tell her he was a police officer making an inspection. He wanders the convenience stores, and the staff there (not having studied behaviorism) sometimes give him food for free in the belief this might send him away.

Both group members and I have talked to Paul for months about how his late arrival detracts from the group process. Paul's entry, often accompanied by turning off the light switch and facile insults directed to all present, interrupts whatever conversation is going on and often shatters my ability to think. Paul can vanquish us all at will. But over time, he has developed a conflict between his desire to frustrate and torture us and his desire to get on our good side, and in recent months he has started coming into the group room nearer to the starting time. The first time this happened, he came into the room before the start of group and hid under a table, where he stayed silent for several minutes and then began making pig noises. From some out-of-awareness wellspring of my training, I had the presence to comment that coming to group on time was something new, valuable, and interesting for Paul, rather than just sighing or scowling at the noise, and I think Paul heard my comment as it was meant. It did take him about five minutes to stop disrupting the group with his noises, though.

When he is present in the group, Paul is often - though not always - extremely hyperactive. He is up from his chair or rocks dangerously back and forth in it. He moves around the room, plays with toys in the room, and sometimes throws food wrappers or other objects he has brought or found. He leaves the room frequently to go to the bathroom, hangs out in the waiting room, or gossips or flirts with the office staff. He play-punches other group members, who sometimes laugh, sometimes frown, and sometimes get angry with him for this. He will interrupt others who are speaking about a personal problem to ask them for money. He is always on the border between play and aggression, but has never seriously hurt anyone in group in the physical sense.

Though I often question my sanity for this, my stance with these behaviors is the classical psychoanalytic stance, focused more on interpretation than control. (I will certainly make a comment, with a tone that communicates I am both serious and competent, interdicting Paul from anything really dangerous. Immediately after such a comment, he will typically look at me as if I was a fool for believing he was really going to cause any harm.) What I believe I am able to get therapeutically from this stance is that it fosters a growing sense in Paul that in group he is taken seriously and deeply respected. An alliance is made with that part of him, which is small but discernable and growing, that also wants to understand why he does what he does, and that wants to make changes in his behavior patterns.

When Paul does sit down and talk, he will go on for a long time once he has the floor. It is hard for anyone to get a word in (though by now we have worked on this a lot and he will let others take the floor when they communicate that they are both needy and serious). Sometimes he discusses actual lived experiences that he is trying to process and sort out, but more often what he tells are wild lies. In addition to the stories I have indicated previously, he has also told us that he is fabulously wealthy and that he has had any number of jobs that either he has never had, or from which he has been fired. (Paul has little sense of numeric quantity or of time - psychodynamically significant deficits, in that, developmentally, these are often the first achievements of children who begin to invest in a desire to master the world around them.) He has told us that all kinds of famous, powerful and important people know him and have intervened to help him when he has needed assistance. I have also observed Paul telling these kinds of stories to child patients waiting for their therapy sessions in the clinic waiting room. Often these children, some of the clinic's toughest customers, have been charmed by Paul; other times they seem to be raptly confused.

I think Paul's stories flow from a sense that we will not accept him or like him if he shows us his real self, so he creates a false self that he thinks will impress us. He does not realize that by concocting these stories he is showing us his real self in a way that is all too raw and vivid. Over and over again, I have told Paul his stories are almost impossible to believe. (I never can seem to leave out the "almost." Truth is stranger than fiction. Who knows? And therapy seems to proceed best if there is always a certain element of ambiguity.) At first he would frame these comments of mine as if I had intended them as confrontations rather than observations, and he would react with intense rage. Now, he is sometimes more able to accept the comments, and - even less frequently, but often enough to be noticeable - agree that he might have misunderstood something because of his disabilities. The first time Paul said this, his vulnerability and authenticity were poignant, though more heartbreaking than inspiring. Therapy is risky business. In a moment without defenses, he seemed likable and pleasant, but at the same time I was in touch with just how primitive and empty his life is. Was I helping or harming by challenging his stories? It is a theme he and I continue to explore.

Not very far under the surface, Paul is very connected to me and to the other group members. Concrete evidence of this began to emerge in the third year of therapy when Paul began bringing food to the group sessions, usually French fries or potato chips, which he doled out a few at a time to everyone who wanted some. Some of this seemed to be about wanting to be powerful and in control - the giver (or, in his playful and provocative moments, withholder) of food. Paul's facial expression and body language made clear that buying, bringing and sharing food was something he took very seriously. Before he could possibly say anything to us about how much he cared about us, he demonstrated this by giving us food which he had purchased with the very small amount of money he has to spend. I have also wondered whether this was Paul's way of showing us, over and over, that he has never really felt he has been "fed".

Paul's progress and lack of progress in therapy. There are many tensions in working in this psychoanalytic psychotherapy with patients like Paul. He himself communicates very little to me about what is going on in his external life. Most of the time he does not, or will not, tell me when he has been fired from a job, or what life is like at home.

A natural tendency would be to have regular communication with others about him; yet this has proved impossible with the parents, and I have been reluctant to speak very often with his vocational program staff. My sense is that, for me to have a chance of being effective with Paul, it is important for him to know that others are not "telling on him" to me. Part of him knows he often lies to me, and enjoys the playful quality of this, though at other times he is ashamed of what he is doing when he lies. I am more interested in Paul becoming able to think about what he is doing and why he does it, and I am willing to tolerate long years of being lied to and left confused in the service of this aim.

Along similar lines, I have also felt it necessary to disavow most attempts to control Paul's behavior. I will not let him hurt himself or others in group; however, I am not willing to talk to him about something I have heard that he did in the community or at work unless he himself raises it in group. Many people have worked for years with Paul behaviorally, and I am grateful for the help they have given him. But their work has reached a limit, and I see my job as trying to find a way to help Paul move beyond it.

In order for Paul to accomplish this, it seems necessary for him to be free, in the service of helping him come to feel more responsible, in-control, thoughtful, and capable. When he describes having done something thoughtless, I might wonder out loud how he felt when he did it, or what led him to want to do it. When he describes having done something potentially self-injurious - crossing the street without looking, or getting into an argument with a stranger who has offended him at a bus stop, for instance - I comment that he could have been seriously hurt and might talk about potential consequences of the behavior, but then hold back from trying to shape his behavior in any way. My concern is that if I move into the territory of trying to control what Paul does, I might interfere with his struggle to develop the capacity to think; he might obey me or resist me, in such a case, but, either way, he would avoid having to think about his own decisions and actions.

For the first three years of treatment, Paul was about the same to external observers. There were times he seemed a little more expressive or a little happier, but he was no better on the job - no more productive or responsible or attentive, no less playful or provocative. I am very appreciative of the vocational staff's willingness to understand that this kind of therapy is often slow and painstaking. I told them I thought there was a productive process going on in therapy, and that I could detect signs of progress in psychodynamic terms. This seemed to have been enough to sustain their support of Paul's therapy. As for Paul's parents, I think they were mostly confused by what he was working on in group, though I sensed that covertly they were aware that something potentially powerful was happening. At any rate, Paul did not seem any worse; he had frustrated many people for a long time, he seemed to want to keep coming, and no one made him stop.

A few months before the writing of this paper, things began to change. I observed some positive differences in Paul's behavior and emotional expression in group. He pays better attention, and seems more serious at times, not always coming off as a clown. At times he speaks without defense about painful and humiliating experiences. (While he still lies a lot, when confronted he is less angry and defensive and can admit that there are things that are hard for him to understand, and that he misunderstands, because of his disability.) He shows a fuller range of affect and more often expresses what seems to be more authentic affect. He seems more genuine and more alive.

The paradox, and it is a very painful one, is that Paul's work performance has fallen apart at the same time these positive changes have been emerging. At work, he gets angrier than he has ever been, and he is less inhibited in acting on his rage - to the point that at times he has presented real danger to others. He is less willing to follow directions, and his productivity, even with good, one-on-one job coaching, has plummeted. He has been fired from every job staff have been able to find for him. It is possible that something is going on in Paul's home life that I do not know about, or that there is a change, having nothing to do with life stressors or psychodynamics, in an underlying, biological component of his psychiatric disorder, but my hypothesis is that neither of these factors is at the heart of what is going on.

My formulation would be that Paul is recovering his voice, his true feelings, and a part of his desires and his soul. I think he has experienced me as a reliable, empathic parental-substitute figure, to whom he can securely attach and upon whom he can rely for nurturance. He can also attribute all kinds of distorted beliefs and feelings to me, and knows that I will not react vengefully, but rather try to help him understand what he is doing and why he is doing it. I think he is forming real, valued, relationships with the other group members, with a lot of mutuality, and is feeling like he has friends for the first time in his life. And I believe he is beginning to think. He is less interested than he used to be in sticking flyers for pizza deliverers on strangers' doorknobs. He is angry at all he has missed and lost, and all that is unrealized in his life.

In the horrible circumstances of his life, these realizations gain him very little, at least in the external world, outside of group and outside of his inner life. He can have a great insight and then go home to a drunk father, a mother both mean and seductive, and a boring, friendless job the next day. And so his progress leads to crisis, and not to a neater, happier ending.

Discussion

By way of conclusion, I would like to attempt to draw out some thoughts about the relationship between Paul's external life and his internal world, and how an understanding of this intricate relationship can lead to pathways toward helping him in therapy.

Paul's hyperactivity and frequent provocative interactions with others have a quality that, in psychodynamic terms, could be considered a *manic defense.* What this means is that he maintains a level of frenetic mental activity as a way to not have to think about intolerable realities in the external world. Paul does not want to think about the facts that his father is drunk all the time and rages at him, that his mother both distances from him and seduces him, that his job is boring, and that he does not have any friends.

Unconsciously and historically, Paul has seemed willing to destroy his already weak capacity for thinking so as to not have to think these thoughts. This is not to deny his developmental disability or what very clearly seem to be attention problems of organic origins. This manic defense seems at least partially autonomous from these features, something organized at the level of the mind and of the inner life in reaction to his organic deficits and the life experiences they have generated.

People who rely on manic defenses also tend to project - again, a term that has a specific meaning in a psychodynamic context. *Projection* refers to a process where people unconsciously place parts of themselves - thoughts, feelings and desires - that they cannot accept or bear into the mind of another person. I often have the experience that Paul tells me partially formed thoughts, or a facet of an affective experience. My job is to contain these fragments, to piece them together in my own mind so that, over time, they can come to make sense. This is different from active listening or offering unconditional positive regard, although the difference is subtle and can easily escape observation. The emphasis here is on showing Paul that I have the ability to think about what he cannot think about, without falling apart or spewing toxic affect.

When Paul experiences me as doing this, he becomes more calm and also more connected, to myself and to other group members. I also see instances where he can *re-interject* - take back in from me - thoughts about his experiences and formulations about his feelings that are not either/or, black or white, but more complex and nuanced. This has been a slow process, evolving over four years' time.

This process of overcoming a tendency toward manic defense and projection, and development of a capacity to think, enables Paul to begin overcoming his tendency to lie. Paul's lies give him senses of empowerment and fulfillment that little else can. Without these fantasies, life to him would feel even more lonely and empty. In a way, Paul's lies maintain his hope that life might be different for him. It has been important to Paul when I have commented about positive elements in his lies, in specific comments that interpret that some parts of his lies are vehicles for his underlying desires - he talks about being a police officer because he wants to feel powerful and thus safe, or being a firefighter because of a hope that, if he helps others, they will help him. When I can show Paul in this way that I can think about what his barrage of lies and fragmented feelings and desires might mean, over time, he becomes more able to think about what they are all about too. At such points, he no longer needs to tell lies.

I have attempted in this paper to describe and explicate some of the elegant and complex intertwinings between Paul's internal and external realities. Attempting to understand them (as a full or complete understanding may never be achievable) can be useful in many ways.

At times, a moment of deep and exact insight can in itself be transformative for Paul. Other times, an insight I arrive at in my own mind can help me frame an intervention, either in my direct therapeutic work with Paul or in my occasional contacts with his vocational staff; or an insight can sensitize me to thinking about what Paul is saying in a different way, perhaps correcting an incorrect understanding I have held.

However, to think in this manner, I find that I need to assume a position of neutrality between Paul's inner life and his external realities. When thinking about a piece of his behavior or a feeling he has had, I do not want to be too quick to ascribe the source to his mental activity, or to the life experience that provoked it. Neither side of the equation is unimportant. What I am arguing is that both have to be made dynamic - understood in terms of motion, conflicts, tensions, and contradictions that can be thought about. At such hard-won moments, leverage for change can increase.

For example, a few months ago Paul was not watching where he was going and ran into two other persons at a bus stop. He fell and hurt his arm. An ambulance came and brought him to a local hospital. He was in significant pain, confused about what was going on around him and upset and agitated that he was confused. Simultaneously he was delighted with the attention and the adventure of it all. He was treated in the emergency room and released. He told the group about this incident in great detail, though with no real upset and with odd chronology and missing details that were so confusing, that it took us weeks to piece together what had happened. Paul became profoundly upset when he received a bill from the hospital a few weeks ago. This was a mistake - he has public insurance (Medicaid) that pays for the whole cost, and the hospital should have billed his insurance directly. Paul got a bill that said he owed several hundred dollars. His parents raged at him. He could not read the bill and feared he had done something wrong. He also seemed to feel guilty about experiencing a flash of delight that he had done something that upset his parents. At the same time, the association between the bill and his adventure colored his experience - what had seemed exciting, and what had felt like a victory over circumstance (he was not badly hurt, after all), had now become something he had done that was perceived by him as unacceptable.

In the telling, Paul was enraged to a point approaching his total loss of control. He threatened another group member and almost hit him with a slamming door. He began rubbing his wrist against the sharp corner of a filing cabinet. My comments were that Paul was treating the group member the way he was feeling; that I could see how upset he was (that is, he was expressing rather than suppressing or dissociating his feelings); that it seemed it was very hard for him to get a bill he could not read; and that maybe we could think together in group about what to do.

What these remarks seemed to do was to draw our attention to a point where the inner and the external intercepted. Paul could perceive connections between his feelings, his thoughts and what had happened, and - perhaps because I had not tried to "put a spin on" either what he felt or what had happened, but just had tried to think with him about the meaning and experience of it all - began to calm and explore alternatives.

I want to close by pointing out that, at a moment in therapy such as I have just described, my own desires and motivations as a therapist became crucial. If I had been too burdened by preconceptions or history, or too focused on controlling Paul's behaviors, I do not think I could have sensed what was available for therapeutic work at the moment, or that Paul could have taken advantage of the possibilities for insight and change that were present.

This is not to imply that I came to the moment emotionally neutral. I was acutely aware, as Paul struggled to tell this anecdote, of the horror of his life - the emptiness he often experiences, the thoughtless and careless attitude he often enacts, the dangers he experiences and inflicts, his many cognitive deficits, the abuse he suffers from persons and institutions who treat him mindless of their impact, the hatreds he feels and their palpable intensity - the integral component I could bring that was different was a passion to understand.

References

Altman, N. (1995). *The analyst in the inner city: Race, class, and culture through a psychoanalytic lens*. Hillsdale, NJ: Analytic Press.

Blotzer, M.A., & Ruth, R. (1996). *Sometimes you just want to feel like a human being: Case studies in empowering psychotherapy with people with disabilities*. Baltimore: Paul Brookes.

Freud, S. (1916-1917/1965). *Introductory lectures on psychoanalysis.* (Standard eds. 15, 16). London: Hogarth.

Heinemann, E., & De Groef, J. (Eds.). (1997). *Psychoanalyse und geistige Behinderung.* Mainz: Matthias Grunewald-Verlag .

Ruth, R. (1995). Some recent trends in psychoanalysis and their relevance for treating persons with mental retardation. In A. Dosen, A. van Gennep & G. Zwanikken (Eds.), *Proceedings of the First Congress of the European Association for Mental Health in Mental Retardation. (p. 122).* Leiden, The Netherlands: Logon.

Shapiro, E.A. (Ed.). (1997). *The inner world in the outer world: Psychoanalytic perspectives.* New Haven: Yale University Press.

Sinason, V. (1992). *Mental handicap and the human condition.* London: Free Association Books.

Sinason, V. (1986). *Secondary mental handicap and its relationship to trauma. Psychoanalytical Psychotherapy 2,* 131-154.

CHAPTER SEVEN

FAMILY THERAPY: SUPPORTING PARENTS OF A YOUNG ADULT WITH DUAL DIAGNOSIS DURING THE TRANSITION TO ADULTHOOD

Louis Lindenbaum, Ed.D.

Introduction

It is apparent that in raising a child with developmental disabilities, dealing with normative life events and transitions is a lifelong process of adjustment and adaptation at a very high level.

Mrs. Max A. Murray (1970), Past President, Virginia ARC states: "The greatest single need of parents of mentally retarded children is constructive professional counseling at various stages in the child's life which will enable the parents to find the answers to their own individual problems to a reasonably satisfactory degree...we need guidance from someone who can help us see that this thing which has happened to us, even though it may be a life-shaking experience does not of necessity have to be a life-breaking one."

This continuous effort to adjust and adapt at such a high level may be impossible. Therefore, the times of increased vulnerability do not necessarily have to mean weakness, insufficiency or pathology, but may be the result of multiple social strains, discrimination, lack of resources and lack of services (Hennicke & Bradl, 1990). Professionals should never deny dysfunction in the family when it is there, but on the other hand, should never assume it either.

Zetlin and Turner (1985) indicate that the adolescent developmental period for people with developmental disabilities is a unique stage of growth. It is a time of increased stress for them as they struggle to determine their relationship to society and the roles they will assume. Also, because parents are uncertain or in conflict as to what their adolescent with developmental disabilities' role will be, they are unsure as to how to prepare their teenager for this transition to adulthood.

This is not only a challenge for the person with developmental disabilities and his/her family but for the professional who is committed to supporting them during this transition period. In "*Elements of Family-Centered Care*" Sharon

Spano (1995) discusses the philosophical framework, goals, underlying assumptions and challenges faced by the family members as well as the professionals in this process. Spano (1995) indicates that philosophical framework of *Family Centered Care* recognizes that the challenge of a child with developmental delay not only impacts the psychosocial status of the child but also has an impact on the parents, siblings and extended family members. The ultimate goal is to empower family members to take responsibility for their own lives. The underlying assumption of service delivery is that every family member is doing the best he or she can, given what they know. Each family will cope with the challenge of a child with special needs in a different way, and it is critical that the professional is accepting and nonjudgmental about where the family is in the process of meeting these challenges. She points out that family members should never be judged for where they are in the process. The professional has the challenge of assisting the family in meeting the unique needs of the child, and this challenge must be met with emphasis on the strengths and resources in the family.

It is important for the professional to recognize and acknowledge that the family is the constant in the child's life while the service systems and personnel within those systems change. Therefore, the ultimate responsibility for addressing a child's health, developmental, social and emotional needs lies with the family. As a result, the service system and professionals must work to support families in their efforts to function as "primary decision makers, caregivers, teachers and advocates for their child" (Spano, 1995).

Historical Perspective

In "*Rethinking Parent and Professional Relationships*," Sobsey, (1996a) states: "Parents of children with disabilities have been described as chronically stressed, more likely to abuse, grieving for the non-disabled child that they had hoped for, more likely to divorce, having difficulty with attachment, denying the reality of their children's disability and angry at themselves and others, by professional researchers and clinicians..."

He goes on to state that these stereotypes are either poorly supported or in actuality contradicted by empirical research, only partly true or reflect professional myths about people with disabilities and their families. Even when parents report positive changes in their lives as a result of parenting a child with a disability, many times clinicians will ignore these reports or treat them as a symptom of some underlying pathological process.

The historical perspective is that the initial reaction of parents to having a child with developmental disabilities is his or her passing through certain stages, such as shock, anger, sadness. These stages may reappear at other times later in life. Although these intense feelings of shock and grief may lessen over time, parents are left with a lifelong "chronic sorrow" (Olshansky, 1982). Research studies on the adjustment of families with children who have developmental disabilities focused on the negative impact that these children have on the families.

The clinical literature describes "grieving" as the parents' emotional response to their child being diagnosed as developmentally disabled. The primary cause for this grief is the loss of the fantasized "normal" child and this loss will re-emerge during periods of developmental and transitional crises. Wikler (1981) found that when a discrepancy emerges between what parents expect of a child's development and of parenting, as opposed to what actually takes place when rearing a mentally retarded child, a crisis may be precipitated.

Reuben Hill's ABCX model describes the process of family stress in basic theoretical terms. This family stress theory focuses on three variables: Stressor or the provoking event (A-factor); the meaning attached to the event by the family, individually and collectively (B-factor); family's resources (C-factor) and the degree of stress or crisis (X-factor). The extent to which families experience crises is seen as being mediated by the familial interpretation of the stressor event and the familial resources available for managing that stressor event (Hill, 1958).

Birenbaum (1971) states there is a prolonged burden of care whereby developmentally disabled children have dependency needs of a longer duration than do "normal" children. As a consequence, mothers of older retarded children cannot look forward to engaging in activities comparable to those of parents of "normal" children now adult age. A second thesis of the paper by Wikler (1981) indicates that the various stresses experienced by families of mentally retarded children are exacerbated over time by unexpected discrepancies between what might have been and what is.

In his review of this literature, Moroney (1986) found four views that professionals have toward families with disabled members: a) The family is part of the problem, b) the family is a resource to the disabled person, c) the family is a team participant; and d) the family is in need of resources.

In the cases of persons with dual diagnoses, the problem for families is that the mental retardation and mental health systems have divergent viewpoints, and there is no real communication across the systems. According to Moroney (1986), the mental retardation system uses an educational approach and provides concrete services. Professionals who work with people who have mental retardation tend to view families as members of the treatment team and recognize the pressures associated with having a dually diagnosed family member along with the need for practical supports. On the other hand, the mental health system applies the psychiatric model to the dually diagnosed persons and their families with emphasis on pathology. Families are viewed as part of the problem with little emphasis on their participation on the treatment team. In this scenario, the family experiences a great deal of frustration attempting to deal with both systems simultaneously.

More Recent "Enlightened" Perspectives

In the past, research studies on the adjustment of families with children who have developmental disabilities focused primarily on the negative impact that those children have on the families. However when these studies were done, the results indicated that when social class was held constant, the presence of a developmentally disabled child in a family was not associated with increased rates of alcoholism, depression, physical illness or divorce. (Wikler, Wasow, & Hatfield, 1983) In fact, the only observed effects were increased risk of social isolation for the family, increased stress experienced by the primary caregiver (usually the mother), and an increased tendency for adolescent siblings who share the burden of care to develop problems (Wikler, 1981).

Hennicke and Bradl (1990) hypothesize that there are no differences between families with a mentally retarded member and other families. However they do indicate some additional considerations: (a) nature of the disability, (b) prolonged and often lifelong dependence of the person with developmental disabilities on the parents, (c) ambiguity of diagnosis and other assessments, (d) social segregation and stigmatization of the families, (e) dealing with specific emotions (i.e., shame, guilt, grief and defenses or denial), and lack of adequate social support systems.

As a result of these conditions, the family experiences a great deal of stress during normative life events and transitions so that they go through lifelong processes of adjustment and adaptation. This increased vulnerability on the part of the family is not a natural consequence of the birth of a child with disabilities but actually the result of multiple social strains, social labeling, discrimination and lack of services. Therefore, according to Hennicke and Bradl (1990), this increased vulnerability does not necessarily mean weakness, insufficiency or pathology but rather the result of the ongoing demands placed on the family to function at a very high level in their adjusting and adapting, which may be impossible.

According to Hurley and Hurley (1987), the process of parenting a child with developmental disabilities depends upon the individual family's adaptation to a number of variables in the severity of the child's disability, the economic and social resources of the family and the internal strengths, weaknesses and personality characteristics of the parents. These intervening variables can reduce stress and actually contribute to the family's well-being.

Wikler et al. (1983) indicate that there has been a bias demonstrated by professionals whereby they have either underestimated or denied parental reports of the positive effects related to raising a child with developmental disabilities. He calls for a new program of research that will consider the new perceptions of these families as successful family systems whose strength has been enhanced by raising a child with developmental disabilities, as well as deriving some unexpected benefits from their experience.

Wikler et al. pointed out that chronic sorrow and increased emotional strength are not incompatible; in fact, many parents of developmentally disabled children describe experiencing recurring sadness as a natural response to the reality, while at the same time they develop increased strength and coping abilities. Professionals should be focusing more on the latter.

Sobsey (1996a) indicates that many families of children with disabilities report significant personal growth and improvement in their quality of life. Since recent research has demonstrated that these changes are real, professionals need to acknowledge these positive reports and support these families rather than minimize them or diagnose the family as in a state of denial or false hope. Sobsey discusses the parents own descriptions of the positive transformations in their lives that were brought about by their children with disabilities.

Sobsey (1996b) states that the transformations described by parents go beyond adjustments or accommodations in that new constructs are created to incorporate new feelings and ideas. These changes are enduring, substantial and perceived as desirable by the families themselves. Scorgie (1996) found several major areas of Transformations:

1. "Personal Transformations" in which parents reported they felt more able to speak out when needed, felt they had a greater power to achieve their goals, felt stronger, felt they had gained in personal confidence, believed they were more compassionate and laughed more.
2. "Relational Transformations" in which parents reported they had met new people and established new relationships, had cultivated an increased ability to see life from other people's point of view, had advocated for others' needs and made a difference and felt their marriages had been strengthened.
3. "Perspective Transformations" in which parents reported they had learned something about what is truly important in life, had developed a more authentic view of success, had learned to make the most of each day and learned to celebrate life.

The study by Abbott and Meredith (1986) has also reported positive outcomes whereby parents of children with developmental disabilities indicated that their families were stronger, there was increased patience and compassion as well as a greater appreciation for the simple pleasures of life. Sobsey (1996b) adds a fourth transformation, "Vocational Transformations" to those of Scorgie (1996). In his own personal experience he has had discussions with many parents whose careers have been radically transformed by their experiences with children with disabilities; some parents have substantially cut back on work outside the home, some have entered the field of developmental disabilities and some have remarked how much these changes improved the quality of their lives.

Systemic Approach in Family Therapy

In practice, the three dimensions identified by Simeonsson (1988) are useful for understanding families that have a child who is developmentally disabled. The Structural Model focuses on the composition of the family, interactions among family members and the family system; the Developmental Model focuses on the family as a developing unit progressing over time through phases; and the Functional Model focuses on the needs, tasks or functions experienced by families as they seek to adapt to demands or events external or internal to the family.

In working with a person with developmental disabilities and his/her family, it is important to combine these models in order to have an integrated, comprehensive perspective, which will hopefully result in looking at the family's strengths instead of only focusing on the problems, stresses and inadequacies of the family. Wikler et al. indicate that families have more successes than failures, and by looking only for problems within the families of the developmentally disabled child, the clinician may unknowingly direct attention away from positive outcomes. Also, the clinician may create the milieu that he/she assumes exists. Hurley and Hurley (1987) state that service providers are inclined to see what is "wrong" with the family of a developmentally disabled person rather than what is "right" with the family.

Hennicke and Bradl (1990) claim that families with a developmentally disabled member who has clinical problems usually presents behavioral disorders such as aggression, disruptive behavior, refusal, inappropriate sexual behavior and other disorders. They describe family members as suffering from physical and psychological symptoms of exhaustion. According to Hennicke and Bradl (1990), in a structural view of the family, the most important problems are boundary based:

1. All interactions and communication of the family are focused on the member with developmental disabilities.
2. Symbiotic relationships develop as a way of coping with the demands but actually divide the family.
3. Triangulations occur whereby the person with developmental disabilities takes on the role of scapegoat and/or becomes the object of overprotection.
4. The transition of puberty and leaving home may result in the family becoming dysfunctional because of the structural change.

This phase of family adaptation described by Hennicke and Bradl (1990) is called "Restructuring". The changes in the family structures are the result of a process of shared definitions and of agreement on solutions and structural implementations necessary to manage familial demands and to maintain the family system. The authors also describe the external context involving a social network approach in which coping with or managing acute and chronic strains on families depends on the availability of social supports given by extended family members, by informal networks (e.g. friends, neighbors) and formal help systems.

According to Hollins, Sinason and Thompson (1994), "family therapy and systemic thinking helps to lift the burden of the responsibility for growth for the individual to a group, the family group including the professionals." It is clear that each family member has different experiences, strengths and something to contribute in assisting the family to cope with and overcome stresses in their lives.

Hennicke and Bradl (1990) introduce the systemic approach into the treatment of people with developmental disabilities and behavioral disorders based on the concepts of family stress and social network. They outline five dimensions that must be considered at the same time in the therapeutic process:

1. Working with the family on the meaning of retardation.
2. Working with the member with developmental disabilities as an active participant operating with individual resources and responsibilities.
3. Working with the parents-to-child systems by clarifying their roles and the responsibility being taken for the member with developmental disabilities by both parents together and separately.
4. Working with the marriage system by supporting the married couple to develop or reinforce their responsibility for themselves and for each other.
5. Managing the problems by making concrete and realistic steps toward coping with present problems, by mobilizing internal and/or external resources, by clarifying roles and responsibilities of the various support systems and by clarifying short and long term future plans for the member with developmental disabilities.

According to the authors, mental retardation is seen as a possible human existence becoming a real retardation or handicap only in the context of family and society... The person with mental retardation is respected as a subject with his own history, jointly constituting his social context... treatment, training and education are no longer related to symptoms or defects but to the whole context which gives meaning to each situation and which defines the problems.

Transition from Young Adult to Adulthood - Dilemmas

In the literature, it is hypothesized that there are critical periods that are potentially stressful for families of children with developmental disabilities. According to Wikler (1981), these critical periods are based on normal developmental milestones: (a) child should have begun to walk (ages 12 - 15 months), (b) child should have begun to talk (24 - 30 months), (c) child should start kindergarten in public school (child "labeled" and attends "special classes"), (d) onset of puberty (tension between physical appearance vs. mental-social ability), and (e) 21st birthday (symbolic of independence from the family).

Parents have reported that following the diagnosis, the 21st birthday was the second most stressful time for them.

Orr, Cameron, Dobson and Day (1993) studied age-related changes in stress experience by families with a child who has developmental delays. Their hypothesis that parents of older children experience greater stress was supported by Gallagher, Beckman and Cross (1983), Bristol and Schopler (1984), and Farber (1975) whose research suggest that stress in families does increase as the child with developmental disabilities grows older. It was indicated that the negative effects on family functioning in families with children who have disabilities may not be detectable until the child reaches adolescence.

Stark (1992) claims that the transition period from young adult to adulthood for the person with developmental disabilities and their parents is marked by heightened expectations resulting from experiences with mandated, parent involved school services combined with a concern about future services. According to Ferguson, Ferguson and Jones (1988), at a time when there should be less parent involvement, the reality is that there is an even greater need for parental advocacy and oversight based upon the unavailability or inadequacy of adult services.

It is important that this transition planning be person centered and directed by the individual with disabilities and the family. However, because of the issues that the person is dealing with, as well as the parents' uncertainty or conflict surrounding the young adult's role, there is lack of clarity as to how to prepare the person for this transition to adulthood.

Nisbet, Covert and Schuh (1992) indicate that dilemmas are created for parents and professionals when there are enhanced expectations during a time when there is also insufficient funds, staff and program alternatives as well as when there is a need for more family involvement during a time when parents would be reducing their involvement.

According to Thorin, Yovanoff and Irvin (1996), a dilemma "occurs when decisions present conflicting choices with equally problematic outcomes for the family. Dilemmas put families in the predicament of having to choose from less-than ideal options that can result in an impasse where no solution is chosen" (pp. 117-118). In focus groups designed to determine the supports that parents need during this time of transition, families with young adults who have disabilities identified a balancing act that they perform in order to deal with the competing demands on their time and energy.

In their study, Thorin et al. (1996) identify the most prominent dilemmas experienced by parents with a young adult with disabilities as: (a) wanting to create opportunities for independence for the young adult and wanting to assure that health and safety needs are met, (b) wanting a life separate from the young adult and wanting to do whatever is necessary to assure a good life for him or her, (c) wanting to provide stability and predictability in the family life and wanting to meet the changing needs of the young adult and family, (d) wanting to create a separate social life for the young adult and wanting to have less involvement in his or her life, (e) wanting to avoid burn-out and wanting to do everything possible for the young adult, (f) wanting to maximize the young adult's growth and potential and wanting to accept the young adult as he or she is.

During adolescence the person is dealing with issues of independence from parents, development of attitudes and behaviors regarding the social and sexual spheres, and development of a sense of self and formation of vocational plans. Moreover, adolescents are dealing with cognitive and emotional disorganization, self-consciousness, impulsiveness, idealism and intensity. For the adolescent with developmental disabilities, dealing with these issues becomes even more problematic because of their cognitive limitations as well as conflicting role expectations from family, peers and self.

Zetlin and Turner (1985) indicate that parents are unsure how to prepare their adolescents for the transition to adulthood because they are uncertain or in conflict with regard to what their adult roles will be. Therefore, they may encourage dependency, obedience and child-like behavior rather then independence, self-direction, responsibility and sexual awareness. The adolescent with disabilities is increasingly aware of his or her own limitations which may lead to conflict expressed in behavioral and/or emotional problems. Adolescence for persons with developmental disabilities is a time of stress as they struggle to determine their relationship to and role in society.

It is crucial that professionals have an understanding of these dilemmas described by parents in order to assist them as well as the young adult with disabilities. In attempting to provide opportunities for independence and wanting to assure health and safety, the issue for the family is "letting go" versus protecting the person from failure. Heyman and Huckle (1993) find that "when choosing to avoid a risky situation and give up the potential benefits of the choice for the young adult, parents may decide to provide safer, family centered activities or downgrade the estimates of benefits to the young adult of the hazardous activities."

The dilemma of wanting a separate life from the young adult and wanting to do whatever is necessary to assure a good life for him or her involves the issue of the parents developing their own identities versus having the identity of being a parent of a child with developmental disabilities. The support a professional must give is to assist the young adult in developing a life of his or her own while facilitating the young adult's involvement with others. This is described by families as a real "balancing act."

An example that exemplifies this involves a 24-year-old female who was placed by her parents into a group home. The mother never fully separated from her daughter and her identity was based upon her connectedness to the daughter, as well as being the mother of a child with disabilities. The mother could not separate, and her over-involvement with her daughter was problematic for the family and the group home staff. Through the process of family therapy, the mother was able to separate by identifying some of her own reasons for staying connected which were not in her daughter's best interest or hers: re-establishing a relationship with her husband and her other children, engaging in other pursuits in which she had an interest and finding a job.

With regard to the dilemma of wanting to provide stability and predictability in the family life and wanting to meet the changing needs of the young adult and family, parents indicate that change and unpredictability is by far the norm. They report that their lives are continually disrupted by problems with transportation, changes in scheduling by service providers, etc.

The dilemma of wanting to create a separate social life for the young adult and wanting to have less involvement in his or her life reflects on the importance that parents place on their young adult having a social life (Will, 1993). However, in order to facilitate this, the parents may have to make the arrangements (i.e., phone calls, scheduling activities, transportation), otherwise their child's socialization will probably not occur.

The parents' dilemma of wanting to avoid burnout and wanting to do everything possible for the young adult involves great effort and time. Many times parents will do the tasks (laundry, cooking, etc) themselves because it is faster than taking the time out to teach their young adult child to do it.

An example involved a 26 year-old male with dual diagnosis, who was placed in a community residence upon the death of his parent. He had never learned to shave himself even though he was more than capable of doing so. Since the father never trusted him with a razor, he would shave him every morning with a blade-razor, and he never considered buying an electric razor to teach his son how to shave himself for fear of him hurting himself in the process.

Wanting to maximize the young adult's growth and potential and wanting to accept the young adult as he/she is becomes a dilemma during the high school years, when the decision has to be made to emphasize academics or independent living skills. During the transition planning process, the student with developmental disabilities and the family must focus on future goals which should include supported or independent living and employment opportunities.

Supporting Families During Transition Period

Thorin et al. (1996) discuss the various ways that professionals can support families during this time of transition. It is crucial that the professional accept and validate the parents' experiences of dilemmas when they are faced with situations where no solution is optimal. Working with parents, to address the issues as defined by the family, is another component of support, as is assisting them in developing creative alternatives for dealing with these issues/problems/concerns. At times, the family needs practical assistance and this need must be supported.

One of the most important components of support is for the professional to give acknowledgment of the family's efforts to do what they feel is best for the member with developmental disabilities and the family, and not to add any "Herculean" tasks or responsibilities that could contribute to burnout. This means that professionals must empower family members, act in accordance with the realization that the family is the constant in the young adult's life and ultimate responsibility for addressing his/her needs rests with the family. The professional must also make sure that his/her intervention and involvement does not add to or compound the unpredictability in the family's life.

It is also crucial for the professional to have a new and positive perception of these families and that he or she views the family systems as successful in that everyone has gained in strength by having a person with developmental disabilities as part of the family. This perception gets operationalized at the initial interview of the family. Hollins, et al. (1994) point out that in addition to focusing on the difficulties experienced by the members of the family, assessment also needs to be made of the family's coping resources: (a) Their energy and morale, (b) problem-solving skills, (c) social networks, (d) practical resources, (e) general beliefs including religious beliefs, (f) specific beliefs, (g) capacity to grieve, and (h) strength of the marital bond.

Wickler et al. focus on specific clinical recommendations to assist professionals in determining and emphasizing a family's strengths. There needs to be a balance between the stresses the parents of children with developmental disabilities are under and the ways it has helped them to benefit and grow. Professionals should ask parents about their child's unique traits that have given them pleasure. Professionals should assess parents' strengths by asking for and discussing their success stories in coping. The authors state that "parents can also be asked what they have learned from their experience and whether friends or family have come through for them in unexpected ways; they should be praised for their creative parenting and be given an opportunity to cite examples" (p. 114). Professionals should assist parents who have been successful in coping to meet other parents in order to foster a communication process that provides families with a model for successful coping and management. Spano (1995) encourages parent-to-parent support and networking based on the premise that family members are better able to address the needs of the person with developmental disabilities if they have the opportunity to network with others who are facing similar challenges.

Sobsey (1996a) focuses on positive transformations and indicates that the critical time for addressing transformations is when the child is first diagnosed. However, he also states that some of the issues regarding positive relationships within families continue and recur throughout the life-span, especially at times of change or family transition. He identifies certain strategies that can be utilized by professionals which will increase the probability that families will respond to a child's disability with a positive transformation. Professionals need to encourage the attachment of parents to their children regardless of disability and to be respectful and supportive of their essential role as parents. This means that when parents are encouraged to act as paraprofessionals and conflicts occur in these roles, the professionals must assist them in finding ways to minimize or eliminate the conflicts.

Professionals need to model positive attitudes by showing respect and taking joy in every child. Professionals need to avoid catastrophizing the potential effects on the family and to respect individual reactions without making value judgments. It is important to reassure families that their responses are normal and that many families deal with these feelings successfully and frequently report the strengthening of their families. Professionals need to discuss family adjustment and transformations within the family's own philosophical framework. Part of this is what Sobsey (1996b) refers to as "appraisal", whereby the professional must consider the way that a family views their situation versus the objective realities of the situation. How successful families are in dealing with a situation is influenced by culture, attitudes of friends and extended family, psychological predisposition, philosophical or spiritual beliefs and many other factors. Professionals must discriminate between interaction and support. According to Sobsey, "Contact with family, friends and professionals can only be considered support when the interactions support attachment between family members and hopeful perspectives" (p. 13).

Finally, professionals need to listen attentively and compassionately. In attempting to educate the professional, Sobsey (1996a) indicates that the difference between the supportive and non-supportive professional is subtle. The tone of voice or look on the face will indicate whether the professional sees the child as an object of pity or that they share in the concerns and the delight of the child. The notion of coping implies a problem but it is the child's disability rather than the child that creates the need for coping. Therefore, it is crucial not to split the child from the disability since without it the child would be a stranger to the parent.

Conclusion

Murray (1970) lists those qualities that parents believe to be desirable in those who give guidance to them. The foremost quality is absolute honesty; others include hope and encouragement. Another desirable attribute is an understanding heart which enables the professional person to put themselves in the place of these parents. A third quality is the kind of integrity and stability of character which enables professionals to work cooperatively with other professionals in the best interests of the person with developmental disabilities.

In supporting parents of a young adult with dual diagnosis during the transition to adulthood, it is crucial that professionals have, in addition to the above qualities, an understanding of the dilemmas described by parents in order to assist them and the young adult with disabilities. The support a professional must give is to assist the parents in developing/maintaining a life of their own while facilitating the young adult's independence and involvement with others. Parents describe this as a real "balancing act" which the professionals must help them to deal with in their work with them. As Thorin, et al. point out, "When families are facing few easy choices, with most decisions involving both pros and cons, they need to have their efforts supported as they make their best decisions for their families" (p. 120).

References

Abbott, D., & Meredith, W. (1986). Strengths of parents with retarded children. *Family Relations, 35*, 371-375.

Birenbaum, A. (1971). The mentally retarded child in the home and the family cycle. *Journal of Health and Social Behavior, 12*, 55-65.

Bristol, M., & Schopler, E. (1984). A developmental perspective on stress and coping in families of autistic children. In J. Blacher (Ed.), *Families of severely handicapped children.* New York: Academic Press.

Farber, B. (1975). Family adaptations to severely mentally retarded children. In M. Begab & S. Richardson (Eds.), *The mentally retarded and society: A social science perspective.* Baltimore: University Park Press.

Ferguson, P.M., Ferguson, D.L., & Jones, D. (1988). Generations of hope: Parental perspectives on the transitions of their children with severe retardation from school to adult life. *Journal of the Association for Persons with Severe Handicaps, 13*, 177-187.

Gallagher, J.J., Beckman, P., & Cross, A. H. (1983). Families of handicapped children: Sources of stress and its amelioration. *Exceptional Children, 50*, 10-19.

Hennicke, K., & Bradl, C. (1990). Systemic family therapy and mental retardation. In A. Dosen, A. van Gennep, G.J. Zwanikken (Eds.), *Proceedings of the 1990 NADD International Congress*. Leiden, The Netherlands: Logon.

Heyman, B., & Huckle, S. (1993). Normal life in a hazardous world: How adults with moderate learning difficulties and their careers cope with risks and dangers. *Disability, Handicap & Society, 8*, 143-160.

Hill, R. (1958). Generic features of families under stress. *Social Casework, 39*, 139-150.

Hollins, S., Sinason, V., & Thompson, S. (1994). Individual, group and family psychotherapy. In N. Bouras (Ed.), *Mental health in mental retardation: Recent advances and practices, 18*, 233-243. Cambridge: University Press.

Hurley, A., & Hurley, F. J. (1987). Working with the parents of handicapped children. *Psychiatric Aspects of Mental Retardation Reviews, 6,* 53-57.

Moroney, R. M. (1986). *Shared responsibility: Families and social policy.* New York: Aldine.

Murray, M. (1970). Needs of parents of mentally retarded children. [Pamphlet]. Arlington, TX: National Association for Retarded Citizens.

Nisbet, J., Covert, S., & Schuh, M. (1988). Family involvement in the transition from school to adult life. In F.R. Rusch, L. DeStefano, J. Chadsey-Rusch, L.A. Phelps, & E. Szymanski (Eds.), *Transition from school to adult life: Models, linkages and policy (pp.* 407-424). Sycamore, IL: Sycamore.

Olshansky, S. (1982). Chronic sorrow: A response to having a mentally defective child. *Social Casework, 43*, 190-193.

Orr, R.R., Cameron, S.J., Dobson, L.A., & Day, D.M. (1993). Age-related changes in stress experienced by families with a child who has developmental delays. *Mental Retardation: American Association on Mental Retardation, 31,* 171-176.

Scorgie, K. I. (1996). From devastation to transformation: Managing life when a child is disabled. Doctoral thesis. Edmonton, Canada: University of Alberta.

Simeonsson, R.J. (1988). Unique characteristics of families with young handicapped children. In D.B. Bailey & R.J. Simeonsson (Eds.), *Family assessment in early intervention (pp.* 27-43). Columbus, OH: Merrill.

Sobsey, D. (1996a). Rethinking parent and professional relationships. In R. Friedlander & D. Sobsey (Eds.), *Proceedings of the NADD 13th Annual Conference* (pp. 37-42). Kingston, NY: NADD Press.

Sobsey, D. (1996b). Family transformation: from Dale Evans to Neil Young. In R. Friedlander & D. Sobsey (Eds.), *Proceedings of the NADD 13th Annual Conference* (pp. 7-14). Kingston, NY: NADD Press.

Spano, S. (1995). Elements of family centered care. In R.J. Fletcher (Ed.), *Proceedings of the NADD Annual Conference* (pp. 13-18). Kingston, NY: NADD Press.

Stark, J. (1992). A professional and personal perspective on families. *Mental Retardation*, *30*, 247-254.

Thorin, E., Yovanoff, P., & Irvin, L. (1996). Dilemmas faced by families during their young adults' transitions to adulthood: A brief report. *Mental Retardation, 34*, 117-120.

Wikler, L. (1981). Chronic stresses of families of mentally retarded children. *Family Relations*, *30*, 281-288.

Wikler, L., Wasow, M., & Hatfield, E. (1983). Seeking strengths in families of developmentally disabled children. *Social Work, 28*, 313-315.

Will, M. (1993). The question of personal autonomy. *Journal of Vocational Rehabilitation, 3*, 9-10.

Zetlin, A.G., & Turner, J.L. (1985). Transition from adolescence to adulthood: Perspectives of mentally retarded individuals and their families. *American Journal of Mental Deficiency, 89,* 570-579.

CHAPTER EIGHT

SUICIDE IN INDIVIDUALS WITH DEVELOPMENTAL DISABILITIES

Lark Kirchner, L.C.S.W. and Melanie Mueth, M.D.

Suicide is defined in Kaplan, Sadock & Grebb (1994) as "intentional self-inflicted death...a way out of a problem or a crisis that is invariably causing intense suffering". This intense suffering is precisely that which requires the attention of professionals and those who work with suicidal individuals. Suicide ideation, attempts, and completion occur in people with developmental disabilities at various functional and intellectual levels.

A review of the literature regarding suicide in individuals with developmental disabilities (DD) reveals a limited amount of information. An extensive search was conducted using *Medline, Current Contents* and *Psych Info.* In 1970, Sternlicht, Pustel and Deutsch published the earliest data examining suicide within this population. While these data bases show a steady increase in the number of publications on this topic, there continues to be a deficiency of information regarding psychosocial risk factors, behavioral characteristics, at-risk populations within varying diagnostic categories and functioning levels, and emotional or developmental factors that may be associated with suicide. Formal investigation of assessment, treatment efficacy, and suicide prevention is needed for this population. A summary of relevant background data on suicide within this population follows. For our purpose, "suicidal behavior" includes suicidal ideation, attempts, and (albeit rare) suicide completion.

The literature shows that individuals with DD attempt suicide and some complete the act. The authors have found that there are similarities in developmental constructs regarding suicidal behavior in people with DD and in non-cognitively impaired child and adolescent populations. Specifically, some individuals with DD do not convey an understanding of the permanency of death and exhibit very concrete thinking processes. However, others are able to relate their ideation in more abstract terms, and are more capable of planning and carrying through with their intentions. Developmental theories in the literature help explain the psychopathology in individuals with DD (Fletcher & Menolascino, 1989; Fletcher & Dosen, 1993). These theories can be useful to professionals in helping to understand the different ways in which people with DD communicate suicidal ideation. Similarly, management strategies for children and adolescents can also be useful in developing treatment plans for individuals with DD. Our clinical experience, supported by the literature, indicates that consistent assessment can identify people at risk for suicide. Modified psychotherapy techniques and other management tools can reduce the painful feelings and emotional suffering at the root of suicidal behavior.

Recognition of Suicide in Persons with Developmental Disabilities

Investigations on suicide in the general population have incidentally identified some subjects as having DD. It was noted that subjects with DD used suicidal methods similar to those in the general population, and that some attempts were completed (Virkkunen, 1972, 1974; Stevenson et al., 1972; Sletten, Brown, Evenson, & Altman, 1972; Andreasen & Noyes, 1975; Holding & Barraclough, 1975).

Benson and Laman (1988) studied people with DD residing in community settings and attending an outpatient mental health clinic. They reported that in both adolescents and adults with DD: (1) suicidal ideation and attempts did occur; (2) methods of suicide attempts were similar to those in the general population with the exception of firearms (given their unavailability); and (3) aggregate presenting problems of the suicidal group indicated a need for strong outpatient programs in crisis and anger management, dating skills, family therapy and depression treatment.

Walters, Barrett, Knapp and Borden (1995) reviewed the charts of 90 consecutive admissions of children and adolescents with DD to a hospital psychiatric unit. Suicidal behavior was a presenting complaint in 21% and was not limited by gender, level of mental disability, or psychiatric diagnosis. All forms of suicidal behavior were noted including ideation, threats, and behavior. Importantly, examples of suicidal acts and threats seen in their patients were similar to those typical of youths in the general population at a similar developmental level. This supports to the idea that management of suicidal behavior can be guided by principles known to be effective in the child and adolescent general population with attention to level of development.

Despite the documented occurrences of suicide in this population, there remains some dispute about the actual rate. Harris and Barraclough (1977) published a meta-analysis describing mental retardation (MR) and dementia as psychiatric disorders that do not have an increased risk of suicide. Ciompi (1976) studied late-age suicide in former psychiatric inpatients and found that the suicide rate was higher in all diagnostic categories except in females with MR. Notable, however, was that formerly institutionalized males with MR had a suicide rate of nearly twice that seen in the general population. The misunderstanding persists among many direct service personnel and mental health professionals that cognition at lower levels precludes suicide. In a survey by Walters (1990), several psychiatrists who regularly worked with persons with DD indicated that they did not believe that their patients would be capable of formulating, or even conceptualizing, a suicide plan.

Reiss, Levitan and Szyszko (1982) described "diagnostic overshadowing" as the reluctance on the part of mental health professionals to attribute a symptom to an emotional or psychiatric disorder when the person was developmentally disabled. They hypothesized that the presence of MR overshadowed the importance of all other disturbances. Suicidal behavior, while always viewed as abnormal in the general population, can mistakenly be dismissed as just another feature of mental subnormality in those with MR, and not considered as a possibly important diagnostic indicator of underlying emotional pathology. A similar concept, "behavioral overshadowing," (Lowry 1997) describes the tendency to attribute psychopathology to learned behavior rather than recognizing it as a part of mental illness. Either of these ideas may help to explain the misconception in both lay persons and professionals that low mental functioning is somehow protective against suicide.

Suicide Risk Factors in Persons with Developmental Disabilities

In the general population, most of what is known about suicidal persons stems from retrospective case studies where conclusions are based on statistical analyses or unsystematic and uncontrolled case reports (Fawcett, Clark, & Scheftner, 1991). In the absence of better prospective analyses, inferences from these studies have become dogma.

While poor research methods for the study of suicide in the general population may be troublesome, the state of available research on suicide in those with DD is also limited. Only a small body of literature exists, all of which is case-based and retrospective. A summary of the available data in persons with DD shows the highest rates of suicidal behavior in younger adults, males, those with psychiatric diagnoses, those living independently, those with a chronic medical condition or physical disability, and those with borderline intelligence or MR classified as mild (Benson & Laman, 1988; Jacobson, 1982; Myers, 1987; Sternlicht, 1970). Clearly, risk factors in the population with DD and the general population are to some extent similar. In the general population, suicide risk has been shown to be greater in those who are divorced or never married (and hence more likely to live independently and have less social support). Suicide is usually associated with psychiatric illness, particularly mood disorders, schizophrenia, and alcohol dependence. The fact that substance abuse rates are low in persons with DD and that is protective, given the markedly higher risk of suicide when both alcohol abuse and a psychiatric disorder are present in the general population (Fawcett et al., 1991). Finally, as in persons with DD, suicide rates in the general population are higher in persons with poor health and physical disability (Kaplan, Sadock & Grebb, 1994).

Males who live in group-homes or institutions show a higher frequency of attempts than do females (Sternlicht, 1970). Ciompi (1976) investigated formerly hospitalized persons with MR living in the community and found that a high percentage of males (and, in fact, no females) had completed suicide. This latter observation is consistent with the general population in which women attempt suicide twice as often as men, but men succeed at a rate 4.6 times than that of females (www.nimh.nih.gov/research/suifact.htm).

Pary, Strauss and White (1997) found individuals with Down Syndrome to be ten times less likely to engage in suicidal behavior than persons with DD from other etiologies. In addition, in their study, epilepsy proved to be a significant predictor of suicidal behavior for the entire population with DD. Harris and Barraclough (1997) reported that persons with epilepsy in the general population had a five-fold increased risk of suicide.

It is interesting to note that in the general population, those having the responsibility of caring for a child under 18 in the household is considered a protective factor (Fawcett et al.). The number of persons with DD who have, or care for, children of their own is not generally known and must be explored.

In children and adolescents in the general population, psychosocial stress exerts a significant effect on suicide risk. School problems, a family history of suicidal behavior, poor parent-child communication, stressful life events, and substance abuse seem to accord the highest risk to adolescents (Gould, Fisher, Parides, Flory, & Shaffer, 1996). In the child and adolescent population with DD, higher intelligence quotient (IQ), a mood disorder, crises at work or in relationships, and teasing by peers tend to be associated with suicidal behavior (Carlson, Asarnow, & Orbach, 1994). Again, a protective factor may be that substance abuse is rarely reported in children or adolescents with DD (Myers, 1987). The risk factors in the general and DD child and adolescent populations are strikingly similar. Both suffer considerable stress when crisis causes the real or perceived breakdown of important relationships, and both can resort to desperate measures if their coping mechanisms prove inadequate.

Assessment of Individuals with Developmental Disabilities

A biopsychosocial assessment and intervention model has proved most efficacious in assessing individuals with DD and a possible psychiatric disorder. Several authors have reported success with such an approach for individuals with DD and a psychiatric disorder (Menolascino & Fletcher, 1993; Loschen & Osman, 1992; Silka & Hauser, 1997; Saliga, Kirchner, & Loschen, 1996). When a consistent protocol is used, systematic identification of individuals with DD at risk for suicide is possible. Periodic re-evaluation of treatment strategies, outcomes, and overall efficacy is also simplified.

A thorough screening should always be done for symptoms such as impulsivity, mood instability, sleep and appetite disturbances, psychoses, general medical problems, and psychosocial stressors. At each encounter, the presence and potential lethality of suicidal thoughts and plans must be assessed and documented.

Based upon various published reports (as well as our own experience) the following protocol is recommended for systematic assessment of those with DD.

1. Evaluation of Presenting Problem

Attention should be paid to onset and duration of the behavior, aggravating and relieving factors and successful interventions to date. Information should be obtained from all who have contact with the individual, including medical and psychiatric physicians, social workers, nursing staff, case managers, allied mental health professionals, psychologists, educators, vocational personnel, family members, and finally, the person being evaluated. Previous hospital records and discharge summaries, child social histories, and educational records are frequently rich sources of information.

2. Past Psychiatric History

Include sites of service and names of all mental health professionals who have worked with the individual; previous treatment including pharmacotherapy, psychotherapy, ECT, etc.; length of treatment, efficacy, rationale (if known), maximum and minimum doses of medications; past and current psychiatric diagnoses; and history of psychiatric hospitalization.

3. Family Psychiatric History

4. Medical Evaluation

Include past medical history with details of treatment and pharmacotherapy; thorough physical exam with neurological assessment; documentation of ongoing medical conditions; names of primary care and specialist physicians involved with the patient, and details of treatment; family medical history; and laboratory studies if indicated.

5. Social History

Chronologically document residential history; educational history; employment history; and history of physical or sexual abuse. Also include family dynamics; quality and frequency of interpersonal contact between the individual and his/her family, sibling order and other significant relationships; overall timeline of major psychosocial life events; personal strengths and specific needs; and current service and support resources.

6. Psychological and Behavioral Evaluations

Include functional assessments; adaptive behavior assessments; maladaptive behaviors described by care providers; and measured level of intelligence.

7. Formal Assessment Tools include:

Reiss Screen for Maladaptive Behavior (Reiss, 1988); Psychopathology Instrument for Mentally Retarded Adults (PIMRA) (Matson, 1988); Diagnostic Assessment for the Severely Handicapped (DASH) (Matson, 1992); Aberrant Behavior Checklist (ABC) (Aman & Singh, 1986); and Motivation Assessment Scale (MAS) (Durand & Crimmons, 1992).

8. Assessment of Suicide Risk

In many ways, the assessment of the person with DD parallels that of the general population; however, attention to the level of psychosocial development and functioning is crucial in those with DD. Important questions that should be asked include: Is the threat expressed in concrete or abstract terms? Does the person have a concept of the permanence of death? Is the person physically able to express suicidal wishes or engage in suicidal behavior? Is the person able to communicate his/her anguish in suicidal terms?

In the population with DD it is not enough to query "have you thought about killing yourself". The clinician must ask the question in several different forms and must have a high sensitivity when screening behavior and verbalizations for indications of emotional distress. Are the suicidal behaviors impulsive and random, or is there evidence of a plan with method and means? Is the person readily redirected following suicidal statements, quickly forgetting about the issue? Has the person recently experienced any added stress (for example, changes in staff, living arrangements, friends, therapists, roommates, employment, education, or general routine)? Have there been expressions of distress regarding work, relationships or other events? Has the person actually exhibited suicidal behavior? If so, is it true suicidal behavior or self-injurious behavior? The two can be difficult to distinguish, but self-injurious behavior tends to have more of an attention-seeking or self-stimulatory quality. It is crucial that all gestures and expressed suicidal intentions be taken seriously. Even if the lethality is low, if the person perceives the action as life threatening, it should be termed a suicidal gesture (Menolascino, Lazar, & Stark, 1989).

Examples of behavior that may have suicidal roots include gestures with pill bottles and medications, use of common instruments (e.g. eating utensils) as weapons, threats to consume substances perceived as poisonous, contact with an electrical outlet or fire, threats to jump from a window (regardless of height), or attempts to run into traffic or exit a moving vehicle. One author recently admitted a young individual with mild MR to a hospital psychiatric unit for attempted suicide. The attempt consisted of drinking a bottle of mouthwash. When asked if the person thought death would result from this, the reply was affirmative. While hospitalized, the individual continued to be suicidal, threatening to "jump off the bed" and "stab myself with a fork". It became necessary to educate the staff that, while these statements seemed innocuous, the patient did expect that these methods could end life. Hence, the patient needed the supervision and intense treatment accorded to any acutely suicidal individual.

Is the person in imminent danger? Psychiatric diagnoses, previous suicide attempts, current life stressors, access to suicidal means, and the person's support network must all be assessed. If the person is unable or unwilling to guarantee his/her safety, attention in an acute setting may be required. If the person is capable of suicide, but not judged to be in imminent danger, it must be ensured that he/she reside or has access to a support structure with 24-hour, one-to-one monitoring and links to crisis personnel. Importantly, it should not be assumed that the person will be safe simply because he or she has a developmental disability. The ultimate goal is to alter the underlying cause of the acute crisis to an extent that the person is no longer at risk of suicide.

Management of Suicidal Behavior in Individuals with Developmental Disabilities

Psychotherapy is important to consider in the management of individuals who have shown suicidal tendencies. The professional involved should be sensitive to the likely origins of psychological distress in this population. Many theories have been postulated to explain the high percentage of psychiatric disorders observed in individuals with DD. Achenbach and Zigler (1968), as cited in Fletcher and Dosen (1993), hypothesize that psychological distress that would result from the limited ability of persons with DD to effectively function in certain social settings is due to overall delayed development. This may explain the fact that conflict in interpersonal relationships and teasing by peers have been cited as precipitating factors for suicidal behavior in adolescents with DD. Distress is a result of incongruency between the reality of the person's situation and his/her idealized self-image and expectations (Fletcher & Dosen, 1993). These feelings are known to precipitate suicidal behavior even in the general population.

In Dosen (1993), Tanguay proposes that a developmental model based on Piaget's stages of cognitive development could provide a conceptual framework for the psychopathology seen in those with DD. Paniagua and DeFazio (1989) agreed with such applications of Piaget's theories, and reported the impression that those in the mild range of MR were likely to remain in the concrete stage of operation, while those with borderline intelligence may utilize a simple level of abstract thinking. These ideas support the type of suicidal behavior seen in those with DD and may resemble that of the concrete operational thinking and limited abstract thinking associated with childhood and adolescence. Levitas and Gilson (1989) also compared children and adolescents to the population with DD, implying that both live in similar ways. That is, both become entrenched in relationships and are limited in their ability to adapt perceptions and behavior to changing circumstances. Their care providers must supply the tools and examples of how to adapt appropriately.

All types of psychotherapy (from psychoanalytic, psychodynamic, and cognitive behavioral therapy) have been used successfully in the population with DD. Many therapists have challenged the historical bias as reported in Sinason (1992), that those with MR are inappropriate candidates from psychoanalytic psychotherapy. Paniagua and DeFazio (1989) speculated that the reluctance to apply dynamic techniques to this population was due to the underlying brain pathology. Perhaps this was thought to preclude the "mental elasticity" described by Freud (1904) in Sinason (1992) as necessary for successful analysis (p. 60). Sinason (1992) demonstrated that psychoanalysis could indeed be adapted for those with DD, and a review of her work is recommended for examples of therapy in those with both severe and profound MR. Fletcher & Menolascino (1989) also reported application of dynamic principles in the therapy of both children and adults with DD.

Case management begins with the systematic assessment of the individual. The behavior should be described in terms of lethality and intent, and differentiated from activity that is self-stimulatory or attention-seeking, self-injurious behavior. Next, psychiatric diagnoses should be identified and a plan for treatment identified. Finally, the acute and future risk of suicide should be assessed based on the past personal and clinical histories of the individual (Menolascino et al., 1989).

Acute management of the suicidal individual is important. Hospitalization is always indicated if the person expresses active suicidal wishes, even if his/her plan seems immature or innocuous. Inpatient management is also appropriate for the treatment of severe anxiety and agitation. If the person is judged stable enough to return home under supervision, the care provider must be instructed to remove all potential weapons and poisonous substances, being careful not to underestimate lethality. The person should not be left unattended, and access to windows, traffic, and heights should be limited.

Clinical experience has demonstrated better outcomes when crisis plans including suicidal behavior management are available to care providers. Staff should be trained to recognize precipitators of suicidal behavior in vulnerable individuals. Since these may be different from those in the general population, training should include common verbalizations and behaviors associated with suicide in those with DD. Crisis plans could be made available to emergency room personnel, so that all those who encounter the individual are aware of optimal, pre-determined management strategies. Especially important is the visibility of crisis numbers to call during an emergency, particularly in group living settings, when part-time staff may be present.

For those individuals who do not live in residential settings, proactive strategies must be implemented. Significant persons who may be of assistance must be identified and available to the person who is at risk. Frequent contact with mental health professionals who can provide information and support is crucial, along with acceptable alternatives if a favorite therapist or provider is not available. In these instances, 24-hour crisis numbers can be helpful, along with simple prevention plans written down on small cards that can be carried with the person at all times. Contracting for safety, while not always a guarantee, can strengthen the alliance between the individual and the therapist. Reminders of pets and others who may need care, or are important to the individual, may strengthen the person's perceived self-significance. Short term plans, for the next hour for example, can be useful and diverting. Frequent pre-arranged telephone calls can ease anxiety between therapy appointments. The therapist must often advocate for the patient by mobilizing support for the client outside of therapy. Churches, volunteer organizations, crisis lines, and other natural community supports can all provide additional structure, support and relationships.

Intervention Strategies for Suicidal Behavior in Individuals with Developmental Disabilities

Developing management strategies to address suicidal behavior requires the systematic synthesis of information obtained during assessment. There must be an assessment of imminent risk of the suicidal ideation and/or behavior in order to prioritize intervention and determine location of care, i.e. acute care settings or in-home management. The underlying psychiatric disorder needs to be addressed and may necessitate pharmacotherapy or other psychiatric and medical interventions. The management strategies that can be developed by allied mental health professional and provided to individuals with DD who are suicidal is outlined with a model that includes: (1) psychotherapy with modifications; (2) person-centered case management; (3) advocacy. In the authors' opinion, these three dimensions are effective in addressing suicidal behavior in individuals with DD by providing the individual with alternative coping strategies. This model provides families and care providers with proactive strategies designed to ameliorate and reduce suicidal behavior in individuals with DD. The ultimate goal is to alleviate the suffering, which causes or maintains the suicidal behavior.

Modification of Psychotherapy for Individuals with a Developmental Disability and Suicidal Behavior

Our clinical experience demonstrates that modification of psychotherapeutic approaches with individuals who exhibit suicidal behavior is warranted and beneficial. Individuals who can participate in basic direct skills required by therapy may benefit from psychotherapy. These tasks include: being able to interact with a therapist; engaging in some form of interpersonal communication; not being actively psychotic; and preferably demonstrating a willingness for assistance. It is helpful if the person is able to sit and attend the tasks in therapy for at least a few minutes with the ability to develop increased tolerance for structured sessions. These are subjective criteria and require observation by the therapist, interaction with the care providers, and a willingness of individuals with DD to try therapy.

Literature is available regarding psychotherapy with individuals with DD for the therapist electing to provide such therapy. The literature describes modifications and psychotherapeutic processes (Levitas & Gilson, 1997; Fletcher & Dosen, 1993; Fletcher & Menolascino, 1989; Sinason, 1992; Hurley & Bellordre, 1996; Tomasulo, 1997).

This section will provide information relevant to select psychotherapy techniques, the use of person-centered casework, and advocacy management strategies found useful by clinicians and beneficial to individuals with DD and suicidal ideation and behavior. Other interventions using various techniques are encouraged. The authors are not advocating any one therapy model over another. The described techniques have been performed with varying degrees of success in general with individuals within the severe to borderline level of cognitive functioning, for whom suicidal behavior or ideation was an issue. The techniques described are used with individuals who have received psychiatric services from an outpatient setting within specialized clinic services from individuals with a developmental disability and a psychiatric disorder (dual diagnosis).

Our experience with individuals with DD who present with suicidal behavior shows that linkage of the individual with a therapist within a short time following the expression of suicidal ideation is helpful to the individual and the care providers or family. This approach is also supported in the child and adolescent literature (Brent & Kolko, 1990). The shorter the interval between the expression of suicidal ideation and the intervention of the therapist, the more likely the person and care providers will develop an alliance with the therapist and become motivated to deal with the issues. It is beneficial when the therapist can meet with the individual during the initial assessment period.

After review of the assessment information and factors regarding risk, a decision needs to be made as to whether or not the person may require individual and/or group psychotherapy. Individuals may benefit more from the individualized attention and time available to develop coping skills and strengthen relational skills during individual therapy than group therapy. However, there is benefit to having the individual in group therapy when the person is not actively suicidal. Yalom (1995) describes that group composition may need to exclude individuals who are suicidal and depressed from a heterogeneous and interactive group. He also describes benefits for individuals with chronic suicidal ideation from participation in a group experience with similar individuals and with an experienced group therapist. Our experience shows that individual therapy which focuses on developing a relationship and problem solving skills works best. Group therapy is then used as an option for further developing and enhancing interpersonal skills and problem solving skills when the individual is not acutely exhibiting suicidal behavior.

Individuals who have been in group therapy and become suicidal while in group, are excused from the group and later reintroduced when they are assessed by the therapist as not being suicidal. The group needs reassurance about the safety of the person and the opportunity to process their feelings regarding the individual's expressed behavior or ideation. The therapist needs to apprise the individual with the suicidal behavior of the group's concern and work toward reentry to the group. The group process provides the individual with support and assistance with developing options in problem resolution which are beneficial to individuals with "narrowed" thinking, and who experience difficulty in identifying options to their problems.

The therapist and individual may want to consider having a care provider or significant other present in individual therapy with the individual with DD. It can be reassuring to the individual when he/she trusts a particular care provider to have that person in the session. This is done only with the consent and/or request of the individual with DD, and with detailed explanation of confidentiality. Time is always allocated for the individual with DD to have time alone with the therapist as well. The purpose of including significant others within the therapy session is to teach both the individual and the care provider specific techniques and to convey information about events to which the person simply cannot relate. It is also beneficial to have the care provider act as a "bridge" to assist the person in practicing skills learned in session, at home or work environment. The care provider can also assist the individual in conveying information and experiences from home and/or work which are beneficial to process in session. The therapist needs to use this opportunity for role-modeling interactions between the individual and therapist and demonstrate non-judgmental communication strategies. The therapist must be especially careful that communication is directed to the individual, so the session does not become merely a professional discussion of care. This approach may feel awkward to therapists not used to having others present; but with specific boundaries outlined, these sessions can be productive in helping the individual to explain feelings and situations to significant others. Care providers can be afforded an opportunity to listen to the painful feelings associated with suicidal behavior and develop an appreciation of the circumstances surrounding the ideation. Their input can provide significant information that otherwise might not be gained.

Often, individuals with DD who are suicidal do not have the necessary skills to label or communicate feelings, to problem solve, or develop options. The limited focus of options and poor communication skills are contributing factors for potentially self-destructive consequences. Initially, the therapist will want to explore and assess how the person describes feelings and provide opportunities for the individual to relate feelings. Often, it is necessary to provide examples of times when the person may have experienced these feelings. For example, "Tell me about the time when..." It is also necessary to interpret behavior and say, "You look angry or sad when you tell me (about a situation or event)." The person may acknowledge this feeling, or he or she may be able to describe other similar feelings. Reassurance is necessary that it is possible to communicate feelings without hurting self or others. Some individuals will think they are "in trouble" for telling about events and circumstances and need the reassurance that the telling is helpful to them. Confidentiality must be explained, and exceptions to confidentiality need detailed explanation, such as in abuse situations.

It may be necessary to teach the individual words or gestures to describe anger, sadness, hurt, loneliness, and fear. Using pictures or a poster of faces is helpful and is a simplistic tool to teach labels for feelings. Assisting the individual to point to a picture that portrays feelings accompanying the suicidal feelings or other emotions is also useful. Active listening skills demonstrated by the therapist convey a strong alliance with and empathy with the person.

Understanding and empathy for the painful affective feelings associated with the suicidal ideation must be communicated by the therapist to the person. Individuals need a "language" or means to express their feelings and situation. The language either can be expressive and/or behavioral. Drawings accomplish this task as well. Journaling is very useful to individuals who can write and who like to write. Picture journaling can substitute for writing, by drawing or putting pictures in a journal. Music is an excellent medium for some people to describe how they feel. Some individuals have been known to sing a song that conveys a particular situation or set of emotions. Others have taped their feelings onto audio tapes. Providing suggestions and methods of communication of feelings as a coping skill for the person is an essential first step in intervention. The process of teaching this powerful skill is one way to demonstrate empathy and show the person the care the therapist has for his/her situation. It literally conveys that the therapist wants the person to relate his/her feelings, and that the therapist is willing to give time and attention to this skill.

Another intervention that the therapist will want to do early in therapy is to identify the antecedents, precipitating factors, and behaviors that signal the person is suicidal or is in emotional distress; specifically, those antecedents that precipitate the suicidal behavior. Some individuals can describe the associated sensations, events and thoughts, while others cannot. Care providers and family members who know the person well may be able to describe the behavioral indicators and circumstances to the therapist. Once the therapist observes, or is aware of the individual's manifestation of distress, the therapist should teach the individual and others how to manage, to develop adaptive skills, and hopefully to prevent recurring crisis.

One set of skills beneficial to prevent or reduce a crisis, is relaxation exercises for managing anger and anxiety. Benson's (1992) curriculum provides excellent techniques for this population and can be modified for most individuals. Our experience shows it is also useful to teach modified breathing techniques to accompany these relaxation techniques.

Other techniques that are useful include modification of mindfulness techniques which are described in Linehan's work with individuals with borderline personality disorder (Linehan, 1993). The mindfulness skills found to be helpful include teaching the skills necessary to observe and describe physical sensations or "clues," as they can be described, which result from strong emotions. These descriptors of sensations include "tightness" in muscles in various parts of the body such as the extremities, stomach, and forehead. Also reported are changes in breathing patterns, heart palpitations, dryness of mouth, and descriptors of anxious, obsessive, intrusive, and angry thoughts.

Some individuals can learn to describe their thoughts in descriptive word-picture terms such as "stuck record, merry-go-round, (or) dark cloud". Noticing and describing obsessive thoughts can be a useful prerequisite skill to employ relaxation techniques in individuals who can communicate these thought patterns. Simple picture descriptions about thoughts can be elicited from the person during therapy.

The concept of learning one's physical "clues" should be taught early in therapy so that the person can learn to communicate the associated body sensations. Most individuals with whom these techniques have been employed have been able to recall their particular physical sensations over an extended period of time and describe the same sensations with consistency. Once the understanding of the sensations is well established, work can begin to implement relaxation techniques or to simply discuss associated events, which can provide the person some relief.

It is necessary to teach relaxation techniques prior to the onset of a particular stress filled event. When approached as a prevention skill within their control, individuals can learn how to reduce stress associated with events that have previously resulted in serious consequences. Acquiring these skills reinforces that these individuals have mastery over their environment, and they can produce internal change. This has proved especially helpful for individuals who decompensate rapidly and who have anxiety or panic attacks. The necessary cues to initiate relaxation and breathing techniques can be documented on the crisis plan and practiced repeatedly in session. The prompting cue should be brief, understood by all, and perceived by the person to be a help and not a "command," or interpreted as intrusive. Individuals will often initiate the prompting they would like, such as "please do your relaxation;" or, they will have a favorite phrase they like to hear. Repetition is a key to success with rehearsing relaxation and breathing techniques during therapy as well as at home. It is important to stress to individuals that these techniques are within their control and can work to alleviate their symptoms of anxiety and anger, which often lead to impulsive behavior.

Once these skills are taught, the therapist can provide verbal guidance to individuals over the telephone during crisis calls. It can be of assistance to organizations for the therapist to videotape crisis responses such as relaxation techniques with the individual and use the video for staff training. Serious episodes can be de-escalated by having options when to employ techniques and having staff and/or family members able to assist the person during difficult situations.

Other modification of Linehan's techniques are based on the various skill activities described in her books (Linehan, 1993). Included are the chain analysis of significant events that may lead to suicidal behavior. This activity is adapted by working with individuals to find out when the problem began, describing the details of the environment and events that precipitated the behavior, and helping the person describe the events and associated feelings. Finally, the therapist works with the individual to see where in the chain of events a particular behavior might be interrupted or changed, and where adaptive options can be employed. Linehan (1993) says, "The overall goal is to link the patient's behavior to environmental events, especially ones that may not realize are having an effect on... behavior" (p. 259). This activity is done in a very compassionate, non-threatening and non-judgmental manner.

Other activities modified from Linehan (1993) have included the steps for increasing positive emotions and making lists of things to do during stress filled times or times when individuals are alone. Some individuals enjoyed and appreciated the concept for developing what was termed "disappointment plans." These plans can be developed with the care providers so that if a preferred activity, such as a home visit, does not happen, then another range of options becomes available.

Additional tools that may be useful to therapists are to modify some of the techniques described in Greenberger and Pedesky (1995). The therapist can assign homework from these resources, which are useful to care providers or family members working with individuals, especially when the individual with DD cannot read. In this fashion, the family or provider can provide support and the person can practice activities usually done in sessions while at home. In general, these activities help the person to identify thoughts, moods and responses. These activities should be done in session, demonstrated to caregivers, and identified to the therapist as helping the individual with homework assignments.

Often, individuals have "all or nothing" descriptions of their anger or other strong emotional states. These individuals need to learn how to identify the range of affect and to identify situations warranting the greatest or least emotion and associated consequences. They can be taught to identify initial triggers and physical "clues" prior to reaching their highest level of emotion. Relaxation techniques, mindfulness responses, and breathing exercises can interrupt the learned maladaptive responses to anger or anxiety. Individuals need to learn how to number the degree of anger or anxiety and associate the number with the situation they are describing. Once this is learned, it is useful to connect the adaptive coping strategies, such as relaxation or breathing techniques, to a low level of affect and explain that the identified lower level of affect is when to start the techniques. Individuals report a great deal of satisfaction with these techniques because they are easy to do, are relatively unobtrusive, and can be done on the job, at home, in group, or while waiting for a bus. The therapist should help the individual to learn which stages of emotion are associated with frequent events such as staffing or roommate changes, fear of enclosed places, employer conflicts, caseworker problems, visits to physicians, etc. These situations are excellent sources of content for role-playing, and the individual can practice the relaxation response while sitting or standing.

One problem solving technique that has been used with individuals with DD in group therapy is titled the modified "Executive Board System" approach, also known as the Job Card System (Zec, Parks, Gambach, & Vicari, 1992). This activity, based on work done by Zec et al. (1992), was initially brought about with individuals having chronic mental illnesses and persons with head injuries. This technique is found beneficial with individuals with DD and who have similar problem solving difficulties. In order to assist individuals with issues related to problem solving that could lead to suicidal behavior, it is important to provide them with proactive problem solving strategies. Lezak (1996) has suggested that executive functioning involves those capabilities that enable a person to engage in successful independent, purposeful and self-serving behavior. Zec et al. described executive functioning as "the ability to self-manage one's daily life" or in colloquial terms "to be one's own boss" and "to get one's act together". The metacognitive activities were described as planning, checking, monitoring, testing, evaluating and revising (Wong, 1985). The described areas considered to be metacognitive processes in this problem solving exercise include: (1) problem analysis, (2) gathering information, (3) planning, and (4) monitoring or evaluating progress toward a solution (Muller, 1985).

The therapist can use this framework of problem solving by modifying the Executive Board technique with individuals with DD. The therapist provides individuals an opportunity to identify a problem they believe is causing them some difficulty and to process various options of solutions that are not dangerous to the individual. This technique is performed with individuals in order to teach a problem solving process and to demonstrate to the person the skills necessary to reason through difficult situations. The process allows the individual to slow down, learn how to specify the information necessary to address the problem, identify the associated affective issues, identify planning activities towards solving the problem, and evaluate the results and consequences. This technique is taught when the person is able to learn new information and is not in crisis.

When performed as an activity in group therapy, the modified Executive Board technique facilitates member to member interaction and feedback. It provides an excellent strategy for interpersonal support, developing options and strengthening alliances with others. In individual therapy, the therapist is interactive with the individual and can provide feedback.

To carry out this activity, one group member (or therapist) is able to write acts as the scribe and uses a flip chart. Either the group selects a group member or someone volunteers to identify a problem. The group defines the problem in a two to three word phrase. The problem is written on the flip chart and read aloud for individuals who cannot read or may have visual impairments. Time should be taken to allow the individual to carefully articulate the problem and to define the affect associated with the problem. Next, the group reviews what information is necessary to address the problem. A list of information is generated. It is important to emphasize with the group that there are no "right" or "wrong" answers; however, there are consequences associated with decisions. This stage is very important, and requires adequate time to discuss. Individuals often want to jump to the problem-solving stage and bypass the thinking through, affective generation stage, and information gathering process. During the information gathering stage, the therapist can work with the individual or group to link feelings to be expressed and items of information necessary to solve the problem. Some examples used have included, "I need to ask the boss about a situation, but I'm afraid to" , (or) "When I have to ask, I get very angry, nervous or scared." Another is, "When I get lonely and depressed, I do..." (the following activity may be harmful to the person or have negative consequences).

During this activity, feelings can be discussed and connected to the concept that anger and anxiety can thwart effective information gathering and hasty consequences, thus compounding the problem and causing further emotional difficulty. The feelings of hurt and sadness are often discussed, and seen as emotions that can kindle impulsive behavior or behavior that may have serious and negative consequences. Once the informational items are discussed and documented, the individual or group can then proceed to solutions or the "What Do I Do?" stage. During this stage, it is necessary to process how resolutions differ when all the information is gathered, versus jumping to conclusions. This part of the exercise can lead to interesting discussions and feelings about consequences of behavior that were based on inadequate information. It provides an opportunity to discuss and evaluate alternatives and consequences to various solutions and to process adult behavior and positive coping strategies. The person initiating the problem can identify the top two to three solutions they would like to adopt.

The modified Executive Board exercise allows individuals to practice in a safe and supportive environment their evaluation of choices, and then to discuss their feelings. The group or therapist can provide feedback regarding various stages and choices selected. It is important to emphasize that when working with individuals who have been suicidal, practicing problem solving techniques during therapy is a necessary step to helping the individual gain skills in creating options during difficult times in his/her life. It is necessary to repeat activities many times throughout a series of sessions.

Interventions such as relaxation techniques can be suggested and demonstrated during the described exercise in order to interrupt the angry, scared and/or anxious feelings and thoughts that can arise from discussion. Using relaxation skills during therapy has helped some members relax and be able to think throughout the information gathering tasks. Performing the relaxation techniques while affect heightens allows for real practice of skills during heightened emotional times. The facilitator or group members need to remind the individuals to do these exercises when these types of feelings arise outside the group. Often, the members can discuss similar situations in their lives when they can use these techniques. This activity has been successful with individuals in the moderate to mild and borderline range of intellectual functioning.

Individuals in therapy may ask their therapists to share the therapist's feelings and opinions associated with the therapist's experiences. The therapist's comfort level for personal sharing needs to be evaluated, as well as the context or experience of the feelings and the circumstances (A. Levitas, Fifth Annual Department of Psychiatry Symposium Southern Illinois University School of Medicine, May 1, 1998). When therapists share with individuals in therapy, they can provide an effective role modeling opportunity and convey how others share similar feelings in similar circumstances.

An exercise that promotes interpersonal relationships in the therapy setting is the giving, accepting, or declining a "gift" of advice. Advice can be perceived as negative and "being told what to do". Individuals will react to the advice based on their perception of the advice and their experiences. The therapist can help the individual to frame advice from others as information sharing, and that one can accept or decline information. The individual is asked to think about a situation which has produced difficult feelings or is a current source of problems for the person. The person with the problem requests group members to provide ideas or suggestions. The individual is asked to listen to each member. The group member with the problem can tell members they would like to receive the offered "gift" of advice, information, or say they do not believe they will accept or use the advice. The group members discuss their feelings of giving, receiving, or declining advice. This has been helpful to less verbal group members who are reluctant to formulate an opinion. It is also demonstrated as useful to frame giving information as a positive concept and have individuals describe their feelings when they elect to decline the receipt of information. The practice gives opportunity to members who develop interpersonal feedback skills, and it has been observed to increase member-to-member interaction.

An activity designed to help members express feelings about positive events, develop insight into needs, and to reduce ruminating and obsessing on worry thoughts is "Prescription for Happiness" (Dossick & Shea, 1990). This activity produces discussion about hopes, dreams, opportunities and successes. When using group facilitators who are physicians, it can be effective to have the physician write the prescription and have the person take this with them. Otherwise, the therapist can provide a form for this activity.

An activity to help with difficult good-byes and loss of significant others is to have the individual write letters to the person who has left or is intending to leave. If done in group therapy, the group can help the person formulate the letter, and the therapist can type and mail the letters for the individual or group, if requested and appropriate. In individual therapy, the therapist can help the person to formulate ideas and can write for the person if he/she is unable to do so. This activity allows feelings concerning sadness, missing people and reminiscing, which provides a means for emotional expression for the person being left. Acknowledging people leaving is very therapeutic, especially if the person has had serious losses in his/her life.

Individuals with suicidal concerns can be given an opportunity to learn to share their experiences and expressions of feeling "bad" (often interpreted as shame and pain). The group and/or therapist's role is to provide support, concern, and acknowledge the experience and validate the person's feelings. If an individual threatens suicide during group, the person can be asked to contract for assistance. This opportunity provides the individual with a forward thinking plan, and can invite support and non-harmful options from other group members. It is very important to process with the others in the group the intense feelings that arise when someone threatens suicide. It is equally important to share crisis numbers with care providers and individuals if they are having difficulty.

When suicide is an issue during individual therapy, the therapist needs to process the feelings associated with the ideation and to contract with the person to not harm him/her self where possible. An assessment of risk must be done. A detailed plan for the person needs to be developed and implemented immediately, including where the person will be in the next several hours, during the night, weekend, etc. The individual should have a copy of the contract and any plans that have been established including telephone numbers to call. Some individuals benefit from trying to role-play, using the telephone in therapy to "call" the therapist. Other individuals may need permission to be absent from work during seriously depressed and/or anxious times, during which times the person will need supervision. It can be quite a powerful relief for an individual to be excused from work, knowing he/she can have some time away from a difficult situation. Honoring requests such as this has proven to be, in our experience, beneficial and a reinforcement of missing work. A plan for returning to work should be developed. The individual may require more frequent therapy sessions (such as twice per week) and an increase in telephone contact with the therapist. The therapist will need to alert the psychiatrist or attending physician of a worsening depression or other diagnosis, and have the person evaluated.

Visual demonstrations of problem solving techniques are also powerful, and they can produce positive results. Examples include: writing the prescription of happiness; giving individuals their list of options from the flip chart to take with them; and for visually impaired people, holding their hand and assigning each finger an alternative with having the person repeat each option holding up the fingers involved. Tangible reminders are beneficial, and feedback from participants shows this is effective. Giving a copy of the no suicide contract to the person, a document where the person agrees not to harm him/herself, demonstrates the therapist's commitment to the person's safety and well being.

Individuals can develop insight into their suicidal behavior and make decisions not to hurt themselves. One individual who had repeated suicidal ideation and attempts, and numerous hospitalizations, was finally able to relate, "if I do that (kill himself), I won't get to see you anymore." This person was also able to demonstrate alternative coping strategies and participate in a crisis plan, which was developed with the person's input. This individual had been in therapy for a period of time, until the therapy finally suggested that the person ought to get a job in the community (or, "real world", as our clients sometimes call it!). The individual believed it was time to move on, and so did the therapist.

Person-Centered Casework and Advocacy

Therapists and allied health professionals will need to employ strategies in addition to providing psychotherapy. Therapists who traditionally are not active in their clients' lives may need to review casework principles. Therapists must recognize that individuals live in a "web of relationships" as described by Levitas and Gilson (1989). Involvement with significant personnel and family that comprise these relationships is very important in reducing and preventing suicidal behavior. Often, individuals have problems with expressing their concerns, desires, and wishes to the influential people in their lives, and little means to effect system changes. Therapists can work to assist the person to access, link and manage their array of supports.

Some case management strategies to reduce suicidal behavior may include: requesting a staffing of care providers and significant others to hear out concerns about psychosocial issues (such as preferences and individual choices) and plan options with the person. The therapist can work in psychotherapy sessions with individuals to develop their choices, articulate their feelings, and to convey what might work for them. In order to implement choices for the individual to be heard, the therapist may need to request a discussion forum. Our clinical experience demonstrates that involving the essential players in organizations, families and systems can alleviate potentially drastic results. That is, service systems often portray a client-centered focus as an array of service model. However, these can become operationalized, and in some instances, where the individual perceives that choices are limited and the individuals may not know how to access supports or request assistance. The therapist needs to be cautioned not to challenge authority, but to offer helpful suggestions and assist the individual in asserting his/her rights and preferences. Our experience has shown that when decision-makers hear requests in a playful and non-threatening manner, they have been able to implement alternatives for changes in employment, work, and living arrangements. False promises certainly are never given. However, individuals can be given the dignity of having their requests heard and having a plan of action, which may have to be implemented in stages. Realistic timetables should be shared with the person with identified points of responsibility, including those areas for which the individual is responsible and the requisite time frame associated. Barriers need to be addressed in a forthright manner, with alternatives to preferences identified.

There are instances when linkage to services is necessary and an individual does not have an attachment to an organization that supplies case-management services. In these instances, the therapist may need to make the necessary linkages and/or assist the individual or family in receiving necessary services. It is essential for the therapist to be aware of services, entitlements, and community resources available to persons with DD who have psychiatric impairments.

Crisis plans need to be developed with significant care providers and/or family members. The plans do not need to be elaborate. Rather, it is suggested that a simple outline be placed in available records of the individual's home and work environment, and sent to the emergency room if this is a resource frequently used. The plan needs to be developed with the person's primary care provider, case manager, and significant others. The plan should include a list of antecedent behaviors that occur before crisis episodes, a list of activities or interventions to try, the verbal prompts or cues to use, and crisis telephone numbers for care providers to call. If the individual has a physician, he or she should be consulted in the development of the plan. This plan should be evaluated periodically for efficacy, and to ensure that telephone numbers remain current. Individuals need to be apprised of the contents of the plan. Therapists can role-play with the individual on how to contact crisis lines and how to access help.

Providing linkage information and resource information is vital to the individual who lives independently and does not receive ongoing supports. Knowledge of the community's emergency mental health system and measures is paramount for the therapist and a crisis plan can be developed with the individual to follow. Cards with numbers and names can be made for the person to carry with them and to place in their home or place of work. Rehearsal during therapy about where to go and who to contact is essential.

Advocating for a person's right to services and access to mental health services is required from the therapist who works with individuals with DD and who are suicidal. Advocacy efforts may need to include establishing working agreements or arrangements with acute care personnel, psychiatrists, physicians, providers of services and funding entities. Advocacy can be a function of the therapist who wants to help develop a system of care that is responsive to individual who have suicidal behavior and/or ideation. Providing information to direct service personnel about individuals with DD who have a psychiatric disorder, can bring an understanding of this population's mental health needs and work to reduce the suffering these individuals may have and the dangerous consequences of suicidal behavior. Advocating for accessible mental health services to individuals who become suicidal, in the authors' opinion, is a responsibility of therapists who work with this population. Greater awareness of mental illness in individuals with DD and a psychiatric disorder, who have suicidal ideation and or behavior is needed. Our experiences continue to show that providers and family members want this information, and they find education and information beneficial to their understanding of the multiple issues that effect people with DD who also have suicidal behavior.

Positive outcomes have been observed when management strategies, including psychotherapy, have been provided to individuals with suicidal behavior. Alternative coping strategies for the individual can be developed, and care providers can be given effective crisis management tools. Suicidal behavior can be reduced.

The literature shows that individuals with developmental disabilities attempt and complete suicide. The authors' clinical experiences demonstrate that consistent assessment identifies people at risk, which allows for intervention. The goal of the intervention is to reduce the painful feelings surrounding the suicidal behavior and to prevent harm. The goal includes providing individuals with adaptive skills and abilities to effect internal change. It is our opinion that acute hospitalization with person-centered planning can be effective in reducing state facility admission, which can allow the person to remain in his/her own community. However, the community needs to have resources available which provide assessment, crisis management, and follow up. There also needs to be training and education to consumers, families, professionals and providers, clarifying that this population can have suicidal behavior, and treatment is necessary and can be effective. With systematic approaches to assessment and intervention, data can be generated that allow practitioners to evaluate efficacy of treatment, identify psychosocial factors that may contribute to suicide in this population, and result ultimately in prevention efforts.

References

Aman, M.G., & Singh, N. (1986). *ABC aberrant behavior checklist manual.* East Aurora, New York: Slosson.

Andreasen N.C., & Noyes R. (1975). Suicide attempted by self-immolation. *American Journal of Psychiatry*, 132-135.

Benson, B.A. (1992). *Teaching anger management to persons with mental retardation.* Worthington, OH: International Diagnostics Systems.

Benson, B.A., & Laman, D.S. (1988). Suicidal tendencies of mentally retarded adults in community settings. *Australia and New Zealand Journal of Developmental Disabilities, 14,* 49-54.

Brent, B., & Kolko, D. (1990). Suicide and suicidal behavior in children and adolescents. *Psychiatric Disorders in Children and Adolescents,* 372-391.

Carlson, G.A., Asarnow, J.R., & Orbach, I. (1994). Developmental aspects of suicidal behavior in children and developmentally delayed adolescents. *New Direction for Children,* 93-107.

Ciompi, L. (1976). Late suicide in former mental patients. *Psychiatric Clinical, 1,* 59-63.

Dosen, A. (1993). Part 1: Overview. In R. Fletcher & A. Dosen (Eds.), *Mental health aspects of mental retardation* (pp. 3-17). New York: Lexington Books.

Dossick, J., & Shea, E. (1990). *Creative therapy II: 50 more exercises for groups.* Sarasota, FL: Professional Resource Exchange.

Durand, M., & Crimmins, D. (1992). *The motivation assessment scale (MAS) administration guide.* Topeka, KS: Monoco.

Fawcett, J., Clark, D., & Scheftner, W. (1991). The assessment and management of the suicidal patient. *Psychiatric Medicine, 9,* 299-310.

Fletcher, R., & Menolascino, F. (1989). *Mental retardation and mental illness. Assessment, treatment, and service for the dually diagnosed.* New York: Lexington Books.

Fletcher, R. J., & Dosen, A. (1993). *Mental health aspects of mental retardation: Progress in assessment and treatment.* New York : Lexington Books.

Gould, M., Fisher, P., Parides, M., Flory, M., & Shaffer, D. (1996). Psychosocial risk factors of child and adolescent completed suicide archives. *General Psychiatry, 53,* 1155-1162.

Greenberger, D., & Pedesky, C. (1995). *Mind over mood: A cognitive therapy treatment manual for clients.* New York: Guilford Press.

Harris, E.C., & Barraclough, B. (1997). Suicide as an outcome for mental disorders meta-analysis. *British Journal of Psychiatry,* 205-228.

Holding, T.A., & Barraclough, B.M. (1975). Psychiatric morbidity in a sample of a London coroner's open verdicts. *British Journal of Psychiatry,* 133-43.

Hurley, A.D., & Bellordre, C. (1996). *Bibliography on counseling and psychotherapy.* Kingston, NY: NADD Press.

Jacobson, J.W. (1982). Problem behavior and psychiatric impairment within a developmentally disabled population I: Behavior frequency. *Applied Research in Mental Retardation, 3,* 121-139.

Kaplan, H.I., Sadock, B.J., & Grebb, J.A. (1994). Kaplan and Sadock's synopsis of psychiatry behavioral sciences clinical psychiatry (7th ed.). Baltimore: Williams and Wilkins.

Levitas, A., & Gilson, S. (1997). Individual psychotherapy for persons with mild and moderate mental retardation. *The NADD Newsletter, 14,* 34-38. Kingston, NY: NADD Press

Levitas, A., & Gilson, S. (1989). Psychodynamic psychotherapy with mildly and moderately retarded patients. In R. Fletcher & F. Menolacino (Eds.), *Mental retardation and mental illness: Assessment, treatment and service for the dually diagnosed* (pp. 71-109). New York: Lexington Books.

Lezak, M.D. (1996). *Neuropsychological assessment (3rd ed.)* New York: Oxford University Press.

Linehan, M. (1993) *Cognitive behavioral treatment of borderline personality disorder.* New York: Guilford Press.

Linehan, M. (1993) *Skills training manual for treating borderline personality disorder.* New York: Guilford Press.

Loschen, E., & Osman. (1992). Self-injurious behavior in the developmentally disabled: Assessment techniques. *Psychopharmacology Bulletin, 28,* 433-437.

Lowry, M. (1997). Unmasking mood disorders: Recognizing and measuring symptomatic behaviors. *The Habilitative Mental Healthcare Newsletter, 16.*

Matson, J. (1992). DASH: *Diagnostic assessment for the severely handicapped.* Oxford, MS: Oxford.

Matson, J. (1988). *The PIRMA manual.* Worthington, OH: International Diagnostics Systems.

Menolascino, E., Lazar, J., & Stark, J. (1989). Diagnosis and management of depression and suicidal behavior in persons with severe mental retardation. *Journal of the Multi-Handicapped Person, 2,* 89-103.

Muller, P.J. (1985). Metacognition and attention. *Instructional Practices, 2,* 181-221.

Myers, B.A., (1987). Psychiatric problems in adolescents with developmental disabilities. *Journal of the Academy of Child and Adolescent Psychiatry, 26,* 74-79.

Paniagua, C. & DeFazio, A. (1989) Psychodynamics of the mildly retarded and borderline-intelligence adult. In R. Fletcher & F. Menolascino (Eds.), *Mental retardation and mental illness: Assessment, treatment and service for the dually diagnosed* (pp. 35-57). New York: Lexington Books.

Pary, R.J., Strauss, D., & White, J.F. (1997). A population survey of suicide attempts in persons with and without down syndrome. *Down Syndrome Quarterly, 2,* 12-13.

Reiss, S., Levitan, G., & Szyszko, J. (1982). Emotional disturbance and mental retardation: Diagnostic overshadowing. *American Journal of Mental Deficiency, 86,* 567-574.

Saliga, C., Kirchner, L., & Loschen, E. (1996) Nonpharmacologic treatment of anxiety disorders: One woman's story. In A. Poindexter (Ed.), *Assessment and treatment of anxiety disorders in persons with mental retardation.* Kingston, NY: NADD Press.

Silka, V., & Hauser, M. (1997). Psychiatric assessment of the person with mental retardation. *Psychiatric Annual, 27,* 170-174.

Sinason, V. (1992). *Mental handicap and the human condition: New approaches from the Tavistock.* London: Free Association Books.

Sletten, I., Brown, M., Evenson, R., & Altman, H. (1972). Suicide in mental hospital patients. *Diseases of the Nervous System, 33,* 328-334.

Sternlicht, M. (1970). Suicidal tendencies among institutionalized retardates. *Birmingham (Eng.) Midland Society for the Study of Mental Subnormality,* 93-102.

Stevenson, E.K., Hudgens, R.W., Held, C.P., Meredith, C.H., Hendrix, M.E., & Carr, D.L. (1972). Suicidal communication by adolescents. *Diseases of the Nervous System, 33,* 112-22.

Tomasulo, D.J. (1997). Beginning and maintaining a group. *The Habilitative Mental Healthcare Newsletter, 16,* 41-48.

Virkkunen, M. (1974). Suicide linked to homicide. *Psychiatric Quarterly, 48,* 276-82.

Virkkunen, M. (1972). On suicides by disability pensioners. *Acta Soc-Med, 1,* 1-8.

Walters, A.S., Barrett, R.P., Knapp, L.G., & Borden, M.D. (1995). Suicidal behavior in children and adolescents with mental retardation. *Research in Developmental Disabilities, 16,* 85-96,

Walters, R.M. (1990). Suicidal behavior in severely mentally handicapped patients. *British Journal of Psychiatry, 157,* 444-446.

Wong, B.Y.L. (1985). Metacognition and learning disabilities. *Instructional Practices, 2,* 137-180. *www.nihn.nih.gov/research/suifact.htm,* p.6.

Yalom, I.D. (1995) *The theory and practice of group psychotherapy.* New York: Basic Books.

Zec, R., Parks, R., Gambach, J., & Vicari, S. (1992) The executive board system: An innovative approach to cognitive-behavioral rehabilitation in patients with traumatic brain injury. In C. Long & L. Ross (Eds.), *Handbook of head trauma.* New York: Plenum Press.

CHAPTER NINE

PSYCHOTHERAPY FOR SEX OFFENDERS WITH DEVELOPMENTAL DISABILITES

Diane Cox-Lindenbaum, A.C.S.W.

Introduction

An essential part of the treatment for sex offenders with a developmental disability is an ability to integrate cognitive, didactic, educational, behavioral, psychiatric, and clinical information so that it will ultimately assist him/her in reducing sexually offensive behaviors.

Although we have begun to isolate factors that are similar and different to non-disabled offenders, there are few programs which are uniquely tailored to reach the child, adolescent or adult who is developmentally disabled, and who engages in sexually offensive behaviors.

As current trends of treatment refocus on issues of lack of attachment, lack of intimacy, issues of poor self-esteem and the narcissistic behavior that is the defense against these internal negative feelings, we must focus again on the psychotherapeutic process necessary in dealing with the depression, abandonment and all-encompassing shame which is part of this narcissistic wound. Specific to our interest, this chapter asks the following questions: How can we as clinicians amend, adapt and create offense-specific treatment which will meet these needs? How can the developmentally disabled, dual diagnosed, child, adolescent or adult sex offender integrate within his/her psyche the basic components of treatment which is to reduce destructive behavior and replace it with responsible, appropriate interactions? How can we model a program that will enhance the integration of knowledge, information, and experiences so that the offender involved will be encouraged to unmask this distorted sense of self?

Psychotherapy for persons with disabilities is noted as a relationship between a client and a therapist who engage in an interpersonal process through a systematic method to achieve the established goal in the client's emotions, thoughts, and behavior.

Goals of psychotherapy are:

1) Having a better understanding and acceptance of a disability
2) Improving impulse control and frustration tolerance
3) Developing appropriate expressions of feelings and emotions
4) Improving independent decision making
5) Increasing self-reliance
6) Improving interpersonal relationships
7) Improving social skills
8) Increasing coping skills to deal with stress

We understand that in order to achieve these goals there are principles for achieving a therapeutic relationship such as:

1) Empathetic understanding
2) Respect and acceptance of the person we are working with
3) Therapeutic genuineness
4) Concreteness
5) Accepting the circumstances of the life of the client
6) Consistency
7) Confidentiality
8) Expressing genuine interest in the person's life

Through this process a respectful, collaborative therapeutic alliance will form which is and can be a powerful clinical intervention. And yet, when we are to provide effective treatment approaches for a population of children, adolescents and adults who have engaged in serious sexually acting out behaviors, we have few resources for treatment. The majority of the population is remanded to the most restrictive environment with no recourse for treatment.

Traditionally, clinical treatment for persons who sexually offend has focused only on the descriptive aspects of the disorder rather than the developmental and psychodynamic issues which lead to sexually aggressive behaviors.

Another major obstacle to treatment is an inability on the part of the professional community to recognize a sexual disorder in a child, adolescent or adult with a developmental disability. Often sexually violent acts such as rape, child molestation, sexual masochism, sexual sadism and exhibitionism are assumed to be the result of the mental retardation rather than severe clinical dysfunction and personality deficits. Treating inappropriate vs. deviant sexual behavior has furthered our comprehension and understanding of providing appropriate courses of treatment.

With the recent expose of the recidivism of sex crimes in North America, there is a heightened focus on the descriptive aspects of sexual disorders, the cognitive abilities of the offender, the liability issues, the legality issues, the level of mental functioning and the ability to safeguard the community.

Treating people with developmental disabilities who are sexually aggressive and display paraphiliac behaviors is one of the most challenging aspects for clinicians, for advocates, for parents, and for service providers.

It confronts us with two current conflicting paradigms:

1) That each person with a developmental disability has the right to be in the least restrictive environment; and,
2) That regardless of a disability, the safety of the community is a primary concern.

The sex offender treatment specialist who works with adults and children with disabilities must develop a treatment protocol that enlists the concepts of the two stated paradigms. Emotions such as frustration, fear, and anger around the issues of treatment for this specialized group can be exasperating. The responsibility of establishing a therapeutic alliance with the person and their systems, which are often minimizing and denying the sexual violent acts or which do not believe that DD persons can be fit for traditional treatment, can be an overwhelming task. These attitudes, values and policies are generally manifested by departmental systems of Mental Retardation, Mental Health, the Office of Corrections and the Department of Children and Family Services. Each agency tends to disown the responsibility for therapeutically treating the developmentally disabled population who offend sexually. Like the true dysfunctional family system, the focus is on details of the service delivery system rather than on the creation of an effective, specialized therapeutic treatment system which will integrate the mission statements of all departments.

The Social-Sexual Treatment Program has been utilized in community in-patient and out-patient treatment centers (Cox-Lindenbaum & Lindenbaum, 1994). The basic program has been adapted to meet the needs of children, adolescents and adults who have been involved in sexually offending behaviors and who clearly display dual diagnosis.

This chapter will focus on the creation of a "Continuum of Care." The Social Sexual Treatment Model encompasses key components on the life of the Dual Diagnosed person. It creates a therapeutic alliance that reinforces the fact that the therapeutic alliance that reinforces the fact the therapeutic relationship can be a powerful clinical intervention. It incorporates what we know about bonding, attachment, early intervention, primary developmental stages of a DD person (or lack thereof), and the resultant family dynamics (Dosen, 1997). It will involve the complex issues and consequences of sexual abuse and the specific vulnerability of a person with disabilities, and how these issues of betrayal, lack of trust and despair entail through sexual acting out behavior (Garbarino, 1988).

Stages of treatment begin with a contract. As one integral part of the treatment model, it provides a specifically tailored approach that through a creative therapeutic process, we no longer collude in a system of denial, rationalization and hopelessness. Whether it is individual, group or family, the participants must create a safe and therapeutic environment. Initially, there must be minimal risk taking until all members of treatment have established responsibility. General guidelines, such as no physical violence, issues of confidentiality, lateness, absences, smoking, and eating in sessions are to be established. The implementation of specific goals with statements of problems or obstacles to success are reviewed.

The purpose of the treatment is to provide identified opportunities to change. The contract must include the participant's ability to develop alternatives to past destructive behaviors. This is accomplished through a Cognitive Didactic and Experiential Approach. Within this context of the initial contract, engaging strategies are stressed and must be creatively presented utilizing: outreach; leverage-enlisting the assistance of significant others, friends and family systems to encourage commitment to therapy; and confrontation-confronting participants with realities and alternatives of deviant behavior such as loss of programming or jail time, which add to the concept of realistic consequences.

Addressing goals of treatment are also an important part of the initial contracting process. Goals are stated as: understanding and eliminating destructive behaviors; improving peer interactions (making friends); improvement in interpersonal communication; learning to recognize and to verbalize feelings (instead of suppressing or acting them out); learning to monitor one's own and peer behavior; finding emotional acceptance of one's own disability; recognizing strengths; dealing with sexuality issues; recognizing consequences of socially unacceptable behaviors; reducing depression and anxiety; and increasing motivation to become more independent and improving self-esteem and self-image. Such goals are palatable to people who have been sexually offensive children. The clinician often colludes with the mentally retarded sex offender by denying and minimizing the trauma of sexual abuse, especially when the victim is also mentally retarded, thereby negating "client to client" abuse.

Our history of advocating for sexual expression for a person with a disability leaves us guilt-ridden and tentative in our ability to advocate for the sex offender and pursue and develop the unique treatment that he/she needs. The concern of advocates and professionals for labeling a person "sex offender" often takes precedence over actually treating the complex pathology. All of these factors can interfere and diffuse the energy needed to establish a treatment which is based upon the clinical needs of the mentally retarded sex offender.

Szymanski and Tanguay (1980) have indicated that mentally retarded people are vulnerable to mental disorders; yet few clinicians in the field have acknowledged this in their treatment. Services traditionally provided have focused only on the cognitive or sex education programs with the assumption that the "sexual misconduct" was due to a lack of sexual information, poor opportunities for sexual interaction and unavailable sexual counseling. Through the process of deinstitutionalization and community living, it has become clear that some mentally retarded people, who have recurrent and persistent levels of sexual dysfunctioning and who are repeat sexual offenders and have received comprehensive sex education programs but have not been able to integrate this information nor modify their sexually violent behavior. Therefore, the mentally retarded sex offender requires a more comprehensive clinical treatment approach.

Personality Profile and Characteristics of Mentally Retarded Sex Offenders

A person with an intellectual disability is already "at risk" for emotional disturbance based upon deficits in the area of interpersonal relations. Therefore, there are unique emotional challenges in working with this population. These challenges can be caused by internal (pathological factors) or external (familial/environmental) factors. The mental illness is not part of the mental retardation, but rather emerges out of the vulnerability which the mental retardation brings to those persons and their abilities to master and control an otherwise non-responsive world. This awareness of the presence of a dual diagnosis sets the stage for treatment.

Offenses committed by intellectually disabled sex offenders generally parallel those of non-disabled offenders though the manifestation of the acting out behaviors may differ. The majority of sex offenders (including those who are mentally retarded) are not psychotic nor are they misbehaving sexually. Instead, they have serious psychological differences which handicap them in social-sexual relationships, and under stress, they act out sexually (Groth, 1979). Violent, aggressive acting out behaviors such as rape, child molestation, and exhibitionism are in fact "pseudo" sexual acts. As Groth has found, they are acts of hostility rather than acts of passion; they are always symptoms of psychological dysfunctioning. These deficits make it difficult (if not impossible) to establish and maintain adult relationships which could lead to a bond with an adult partner.

Kohut (1994) states that perversions are often driven by enactments with figures or symbols that give them the feeling of being wanted, alive or powerful. He also states that youthful offenders often repeat acts through which they can demonstrate to themselves an escape from the realization that they feel devoid of sustaining any real self-confidence.

Characteristically, the most prominent feature of paraphiliacs in general, whether they are cognitively impaired or not, is the visible absence of an ability to form close emotional relationships with others. These clients lack warmth, trust, companionship and empathy for others. Clinically, these clients are not motivated for treatment. In fact, they do not appreciate the seriousness of the offense, nor do they ever recognize that they have a problem. Given the fear of legal consequences, they are withholding of any information about their involvement in sexual offenses.

Becker and Hunter (1993) state that early life experiences of abuse and deprivation appear to leave youthful offenders angry, bitter and cynical. Their ability to form attachments to others is impaired and there seems to be a distinct fear or disdain of interpersonal intimacy. She continues that intimacy may be synonymous with vulnerability and exploitation. Many become adept at manipulating others.

There have been indications that child molesters and rapists suffer from intimacy deficits and are lonelier than other offender groups. She states the presence of disruptive attachment bonds, and suggests that intimacy and loneliness be a target of treatment for the sex offender.

As stated previously, a major obstacle to treating persons with mental retardation who are sex offenders has been the inability of the professional community to recognize a psychiatric sexual disorder in a person with mental retardation. In an attempt to familiarize the professional in working with the client and this disorder, it is helpful to recognize personality deficits that are exhibited. The following are personality deficits that are manifested by a mentally retarded sex offender which are similar to those found in paraphiliacs who have normal cognitive functioning: low self esteem - sense of worthlessness; a learned helplessness - a sense of powerlessness regarding daily living functioning; an inability to form close relationships with peers - separates self from other mentally retarded clients; poor impulse control; poor anger management skills; high anxiety levels - agitated depression/altered mood states; resistance to treatment; focuses on unavailable partners - enhances rejection cycle; poor adaptive use of sexual knowledge; poor social skills - withdrawn, loner; denial of mental retardation disability - alienation from peers; moderate-mild mental retardation - borderline intellectual functioning; poor coping methods; emotional difficulties in accepting change -rigidity in approach to daily living; history of family violence; history of early childhood deprivation and neglect; history of physical/sexual abuse; exhibits suicidal ideation or gestures which may lead to suicide attempts; and sexual acting out manifested in adolescence.

The clinician working with a sex offender who is developmentally disabled is presented with an individual who has learned to use sex dysfunctionally through violence and who possesses deficits in personality development, social-sexual skills, life management skills and also has experienced significant childhood trauma. By understanding these personality deficits and characteristics of this disorder, clinicians will be less likely to engage in counter-transferential control issues with the client in treatment. By isolating these personality traits which are dysfunctional, the clinical team can develop treatment plans that are focused on assisting the client in the therapeutic process (Becker & Hunter, 1993). The team emphasizes the importance of linking prior victimization experiences and one's own emotional pain and suffering with antecedent sexual acting out behaviors.

Specialists are beginning to focus on the developmental and psychodynamic issues and address how they contribute to sexual acting out behavior. It is suggested that low self-esteem is an immediate precursor to offending of child molesters and that offenders demonstrate a lack of confidence in social interaction.

Most recently, Day (1997) prepared an excellent research review in "Psycho-Social Profiles of Mentally Retarded Sex Offenders." Dr. Day indicates that the mean IQ was 59.5, Brain Damage 40%, Physical Disabilities 51%, Psychiatric Illness 7%, high behavior problems, sociopathic personalities, sexually inexperienced relationships, family delinquency, history of school problems, delinquent behaviors, physical abuse, sexual abuse, high levels of family violence, family conflicts, and separation from family.

This correlates closely to identification of personality deficits such as: low self-esteem; poor impulse control; learned helplessness; sense of powerlessness; poor anger management skills; adaptive knowledge of sexual knowledge; poor acceptance of dual disability; and poor coping skills (Haaven, 1993). Day (1997) continues that he sees two differentiated groups of sex offenders: those who commit sex offenses only and those whose sex offending style is part of a wider spectrum of offending behavior as well as distortions regarding violence, personal boundaries, use of sex in life, age appropriateness, coercion and consent.

Setting the Stage for Treatment

Creating a therapeutic environment for treatment is paramount in establishing a therapeutic relationship for persons with sexual offending behaviors. Not only does it provide an intellectual concept of appropriate interpersonal boundaries, but it also addresses the issues set out as goals.

Therefore, minimally, the setting must be private, relaxed, safe and open; the environment must be conducive to change and relearning. The therapeutic process must be engaging, respectful, multi-modal, participatory, dynamic and active. The process must include multi-modal materials that will enhance learning and experience.

EXAMPLE: Brian

Brian was a 13-year-old adolescent who was diagnosed with mild MR and conduct disorder. He admitted to molesting a 6-year-old child and a 9-year-old child who resided in the neighborhood. His emotionality was flat. He was assigned to both individual and group therapy. We began working with feeling identification: anger, rage; concepts of self were displayed through visual collages made from magazine pictures. Through collaboration with special educational staff, we brought these concepts (anger management, feeling identification) into the classroom.

He began to communicate with many of his own concepts, non-verbally and then verbally.

All methodologies for children/adolescents/adults with developmental disabilities and sexually offending behaviors must provide a concept of a "Continuum of Care." The concept of the "Continuum of Care" refers to treatment modalities working in modem, with all concepts of programming united. Although one modality may take preference over the others, all modalities are interconnected. Group, individual and, family therapies, system support, psychiatric intervention, behavior program management (relapse prevention model) and standards of care are to be established and utilized in all aspects of programming: structured daily routines; behavioral contracts; use of supervision; accountability and responsibility logs; treatment compliant standards; prohibitions against sexually explicit materials, disinhibiting substances (alcohol, drugs), and sources of deviant arousal systems.

All of the above are to be integrated into the treatment modalities utilizing a *"participatory" treatment approach.* That is, to possess an understanding of how each aspect of the methodologies of treatment (group, individual and family therapy) and all the aspects of the program setting (multi-modal approach, behavioral constraints, elements of supervision, accountability, responsibility, structured routines and activities, prohibitions, security, treatment compliance standards) contribute to the ultimate goal of treatment, which is to eliminate sexually offending behavior and replace it with responsible relationships.

One may ask where can one buy such a therapeutic magic wand? The "magic" is in the ability of the participants to recognize their own strengths, weaknesses and to integrate knowledge which is appropriate and non-violent to others and to believe in a concept of a "New Self" (Haaven, Little, & Petre-Miller, 1990).

All of the above must be embraced with clinicians who can believe in a concept of the "New Self" and yet carefully and cautiously be aware of the personality deficits and characteristics of children/adolescents/adults who offend sexually.

The treatment alliance, therefore, begins with the patient/person and the therapist at the center. However, with careful judgment in manner and process, the therapist must integrate the key life systems into the therapeutic alliance. This must be done with respect, dignity, privacy and carefully planning and sensitivity to all the needs of the individual or group members in treatment. In order to achieve this principle of treatment effectively, all parties are equally involved in dynamics of supervision, transferential and counter-transference issues. The medium of communication is carefully coordinated by the principles of the therapeutic process.

EXAMPLE: Brandon

Brandon had a history of sexual offending behaviors against children for which he was remanded to an institution for developmentally disabled adults. As he began a more intensive group treatment program, he still was a teen who did not realize the level of dangerousness and violence associated with past sexual acts. Through his advocate's persuasion and insistence of his "rights," Brandon sought to exercise these rights by participating in Special Olympics for adults. Although the therapeutic community seriously advised against it, Brandon was allowed to participate under the explanation of being "constantly" supervised. Brandon participated in his sports event. What he did not expect was to be housed in a hotel which "lodged" over five hundred children and adolescents who were also participating in the events. Staff assigned to supervise Brandon were not clinically aware of the internal psychological stressors that accompanied his being surrounded by children. The psychological turmoil that he experienced was exasperating for him due to Brandon's initial commitment to therapy. He managed to call a group facilitator whereby he was removed from this dangerous setting. In group and individual sessions he expressed his anger at the staff for placing him in a situation wherein he could have had opportunity to offend and land in prison. What Brandon did manage to explore was his issue of oppositional behavior, "exercising his rights," causing splitting within the team and his clear dependence on others. Within several months of intensive therapy and support from group members, Brandon will carefully identify possible antecedents both internal and external to sexually acting out behavior. He will also appropriately reprimand staff for denying his vulnerabilities to sexual acting out behaviors.

Diagnostic Evaluation and Assessment

The assessment process is an integral part of the clinical treatment of the sexual offender who has mental retardation. It is an on-going process which needs constant review. The assessment process is a tool to be utilized by the clinician to assist in identifying the psychological deficits of the client and the distortions that they possess which lead them to sexually acting out behaviors. The information accumulated should be utilized for treatment and placement planning. A major issue for the clinical team is the immediacy of supervision both in the short term and in the future. A recommendation for a more restrictive placement may be part of the initial assessment, so as to keep the client and others safe from any continued destructive behaviors.

The Evaluation and Assessment process for offenders with Dual Diagnosis should adhere to the basic clinical principles as those that would apply to anyone. The setting should be private and conducive to encouraging openness and honesty. Risk factors need to be evaluated and safety rules for the assessor and the person being evaluated must be the priority at all times.

Assessment tools utilizing picture indexes and/or materials such as anatomically correct adult doll figures are useful in obtaining information. Special consideration for evaluating someone who is developmentally disabled needs to be given in that the individual may require more time with framing and reframing of questions so they can adequately answer them. Also, use of the client's slang words aid in acquiring information and assisting in his/her comprehension of the questions being asked. Knowledge of communication deficits that people with disabilities possess may be useful in phrasing questions. The comprehensive assessment should utilize historical data for its clinical value, determine risk factors, incorporate the strengths and needs into treatment plan, and provide direction for treatment regarding placement, monitoring and follow-up.

An assessment tool should measure gender identification, sexual knowledge, recognition of social cues, ego-dystonic and ego-syntonic sexual expressions, sexual deductions experienced and seductions used, coercion experienced and coercion used, distortions regarding consenting sexuality, and age appropriate sexuality and distortions regarding violence and coercion.

According to the National Task Force on Juvenile Sexual Offending Behaviors (1988), a comprehensive assessment should also include the following: family background, educational background, progression of sexually aggressive behavior over time, dynamics/process of victim selection, intensity of sexual arousal prior to offense, use of force, spectrum of injury, sadism, deviant sexual fantasies, deviant non-sexual history, history of assaultive behaviors, sociopathy, personality disorders (affective disorder), attention deficits, behavioral warning signs, identifiable triggers, ability to accept responsibility, denial or minimization, understanding of wrong-doing, victim empathy, family's denial, substance abuse, history of sexual victimization, family dysfunction, parental separation and loss, masturbating patterns, impulse control, mental status, degree of mental retardation and organicity.

A major contribution of the assessment instrument is its ability to identify the perceptual distortions of the client that lead to acting out sexual behaviors. It has been found that a client who has mental retardation is unable to discriminate deviant from non-deviant behaviors. When clients with mild mental retardation are shown drawings of rape scenes, they often identify the act as "sexual." They often cannot identify the violence in the drawing, although they can describe and define coercions for a sex-education program. Clients who display pedophiliac behaviors can speak of the legal ramifications of a molestation, but will often believe they are only being affectionate when they are in a child's presence. They do not *see their interacts as coercive.* Traditionally, these perceptual distortions have been thought to be the result of the mental retardation, rather than serious psychological dysfunctioning. The ability to identify the distortion that the client possesses can give the clinician an opportunity to enable the client to work with the distortion in group treatment through the feedback obtained in cognitive restructuring. Clients can develop a heightened awareness and accept that they have distortions in those areas of sexual coercion, age appropriate sexuality or what is sexually violent and what is not.

EXAMPLE: Frank

Frank is a high functioning male with mental retardation living in a community residence. Although he could articulate the legal implication if he had sex with children, when asked if a 12-year-old child approached him and asked for directions, his interpretation of a normal appropriate conversation became interpreted as a sexual provocation from the child. As the evaluation explored this interpretation further, distortions regarding age-appropriate sexual behavior emerged.

Hayashino, Wirtele and Klebe (1995) state that child molesters have higher cognition distortions and continue to endorse a system of beliefs that regulate the appropriateness of having sex with children. In addition, poor attachments may be the result of violence that developed in the family of origin and continued to reinforce a faulty family belief system.

Based upon the assessment of the sex offenders who have mental retardation, the results often indicate that they possess poor social skills, poor judgment, deficits in impulse control, dysfunctional family backgrounds, deficits in sex education, distortions regarding consent, violence, and age-appropriate sexuality. The diagnostic purpose of the assessment process is to understand these dysfunctions for the individual and to formulate a treatment plan that will address both the cognitive deficits of a mentally retarded person and the underlying emotional issues which lead to consequent dysfunctional sexual acting out behaviors. Breaking these areas down into workable, treatable clinical goals enables the clinician to formulate a treatment plan with a vision towards managing violent behaviors.

An Effective Treatment: The Social-Sexual Group Therapy Program

Group therapy is one part of the required treatment process for reducing and managing sexual deviant behaviors. Individual therapy, psychopharmacological intervention, masturbatory satiation programs, behavior management, and family therapy all contribute to comprehensive care and treatment.

Group treatment as described in this chapter is a clinical intervention comprised of cognitive modules and experiential processes. The cognitive modules are not classroom instruction, but rather the presentation and integration of this material through an interpersonal dynamic group process. The process fosters a therapeutic alliance that needs to be created in order to treat this complex disorder. The entire program stresses commitment, involvement and responsibility on the part of all participants, both members and facilitators. Through the bonding process, each member will learn to identify stressors and patterns of self-destructive behaviors, and explore more responsible alternatives. Since the most prominent personality deficit of the sex offender who has mental retardation is his/her inability to form an intimate, warm, sympathetic relationship with an adult peer, the prime modality for treatment is group. The process addresses the issue of one's inability to bond with peers, as well as provide a support system in managing destructive sexual behaviors.

The treatment presented can be utilized for all levels and aspects of sexually deviant behavior (rape, child molestation, exhibitionism, self-mutilation). This group therapy program has been utilized for clients (children, adolescents and adults) at both inpatient and outpatient facilities. As stated previously, the setting must provide an area of privacy-confidentiality and integrate safety features for the group members and facilitators. The sessions are consistently held weekly in regard to the day, the place and the time and duration of the session. As the group begins to take on a life of its own, such consistency often lends substantial and reliable support in providing structure to the lives of individuals whose lives are often in turmoil. The group process is and must reflect a microcosm for life experiences. Therefore, group process must be an organized, reliable treatment modality.

Group treatment can be inherently stressful, given that clients need to disclose painful memories and experiences (sexual offenses) in front of strangers. They must also listen to detailed accounts of their own distorted thinking, which can often escalate their own anxiety, anger and resentment. Individual psychotherapy is useful not only to reinforce newly learned appropriate behavior, but also to assist the client in dealing with the emotional experiences when denial and resistance are broken down as defenses. *The psychotherapeutic aspects of treatment and group therapy are best utilized when adjunctive psychotherapies are available.*

Organization of Treatment

The organization of treatment consists of :

Stage I Contract Formation, Feeling Identification, Relaxation Training and Anger Management

Stage II Social Skill Training, Cognitive Restructuring and Relapse Prevention

Stage III Transition, Termination Planning and Aftercare

Stage I

Stage I is characterized by two processes: The Cognitive/Didactic Process and the Experiential Process. The first stage of treatment is highly structured wherein the leader is most active and direct. The main task in the initial stage of treatment is to establish a group with a clear presentation of goals, purposes, expectations and guidelines for functioning. All participants create and contribute to establishing a contract in the group. Issues of trust, confidence and responsibilities are highlighted.

The process of contracting it typically lengthy but necessary for establishing treatment goals. Early defenses in therapy include massive denial of problems, use of projection and affective isolation. Their defenses coupled with the denial and resistance of a sex offender present a very resistant group membership. Therefore, engaging clients in a therapeutic alliance is the utmost challenge. Group facilitators need to present a clear purpose and rationale of the benefits of group without getting into issues. This must be accompanied by excellent engaging and bonding skills.

The Cognitive Modules in Stage I involve Feeling Identification, Relaxation Training and Anger Management. The appropriate labeling of feelings is essential to the understanding and identification of the antecedents to sexually aggressive behaviors. Many children, adolescents and adults with disabilities are not taught to express feelings, but rather to deny them. Ability to identify, label and recognize feelings becomes an integral part to identifying antecedents to the expression of sexually violent behaviors. Use of feeling logs such as Benson, Rice and Meranti's Anger Management Program (1986) and logs found in Pathways by Kahn (1990) can be adapted and utilized in assisting clients in their initial ability to work with feelings and feeling exploration. At this early stage of treatment, the display of resistance regarding treatment will be manifested by the member's failure to utilize the logs as an assignment. Immediately the clinician must address this issue and work with the client in his involvement in treatment. The group facilitator is most active in identifying with the client what are responsible and irresponsible group behaviors. The facilitator is direct and matter-of-fact in referring back to agreed upon guidelines and establishing procedural and structural framework for group processes.

Groth (1979) and others have stated that violent sexual behavior is an acting out of the person's inability to handle stress and responsibilities of daily living. Relaxation Training addresses this issue by preparing the client to apply new coping mechanisms to daily life stresses. Group members are directed to utilize various methods in order to reach a state of relaxation. Deep breathing, music and imagery become a part of each group session. Clients learn to spontaneously apply these relaxation techniques to stressful life situations. Each participant begins to identify his/her internal and external stressors in the daily regime of living. He/she participates actively by intervening in the stressful aspects of his/her life. The client learns emotional and environmental triggers which activate destructive patterns of behavior which often lead to sexual deviant acting out. The participant accepts the responsibility of actively intervening in this process. Each client begins to develop a stress reduction plan that must become integrated into his daily life.

EXAMPLE: Ken

Ken is a pedophiliac who is a high-functioning, mildly retarded man who was participating in overnight camp. He was accompanied by a supervisor. The camp he was residing in was populated with young children who were also participants. Ken, anxious with fear that he would act out sexually, clung to the bed all night, deep breathing and playing his relaxation tapes, although staff was unaware of what was happening and assumed he was hallucinating. With assistance, Ken related his over-stimulation and through counseling efforts, chose to return to his group home. Totally unprepared to deal with so many children, he related in group that his learned relaxation techniques "got him through the night".

Anger Management Training is the third part of Stage I treatment. An adapted version of Benson's Anger Management Program can be utilized for training (Benson et al., 1986). Through the process of assertiveness training, self-instruction, and understanding one's own antecedent behaviors, feelings and events leading to anger and rage, the client learns to control his/her emotions and find more appropriate responsible ways of expressing feelings. The group members practice recognition of physical body cues which lead to anger states, as well as adjunctive mood states which trigger rage. Feelings of embarrassment, humiliation, shyness, fear, panic, insecurity, often lead to an outburst of uncontrolled destructive behaviors. Interpersonally, when clients understand how these emotions impact on their daily life functioning, they begin to utilize supportive interventions to redirect rages and acting out behaviors. Non-sexual incidents, such as feeling humiliated, belittled and condescended to at work can lead to serious acting out episodes involving sexual coercion. Understanding antecedent triggers, sexual or not, assist in managing anger and raising the client's consciousness as to his/her internal state which may lead to destructive sexual behaviors.

During this period of group work, clients begin to identify sources of rage which are unique to a sex offender who is developmentally disabled. The expression of discomfort and anger regarding his/her own cognitive limitations (mental retardation, learning disability, physical disability) emerge. The family's approach to his/her limitations are often explored and feelings of rage and pain emerge regarding placement issues. Review of the client's family dysfunctioning and his/her own victimization (physical, psychological and/or sexual abuse) become apparent (Abel & Becker, 1984). As clients begin to share life experiences, an engaging and bonding factor becomes the identified similarity among members and how they have had to cope with growing up as a people with mental retardation; the emotional alienation and denial is replaced by some feelings of belonging.

The group facilitators are focused on exploring issues and how they impact upon the clients' negative cycle behaviors. The introduction of focused feedback points out how one's rage affects one's cycle of abuse. Facilitators need to employ empathetic, sensitive listening while addressing realities. The final aspects of Stage I of Treatment are an important factor of the group process as members present issues which are real to them and contribute to the group's having a life of its own.

As Stage II of Treatment is approached, each member's demonstration of involvement, commitment and responsibilities for treatment need to be evaluated. This is worked out by each member expressing his/her progress with his/her established needs. This self-evaluation is reviewed by the group as a whole and feedback from peers is presented. Integration of the feedback from peers is then reframed as goals for Stage II of Treatment are set.

Stage II

Stage II of Treatment utilizes Social Skill Training and Cognitive Restructuring/Relapse Prevention.

According to Abel and Becker (1984), 40.8% of child molesters, as well as 46.9% of rapists had poor social skills. Given the impact of poor social skill development on persons with mental retardation in general and sex offenders in particular, social skill training is one of the most important forms of treating major personality deficits in the sex offender who is mentally retarded. Appropriate social-modeling is presented and introduced by facilitators as treatment begins and is presented and integrated in all phases of treatment. In Phase II, however, social skill training is refined and presented as a cognitive module.

In social skill training the sense of fear and anxiety regarding peer interaction manifests itself as well as the clients' own conflicts regarding their sexual identity. The goals of treatment are developing communicative skills, enhancing interpersonal relationships with peers and giving and receiving constructive feedback and assertiveness training.

Practical, appropriate verbal and gestural greetings (eye-contact, handshake) are integrated into the group process. All levels of social communication presently utilized by group members are reviewed by members, and where appropriate, replaced with more socially acceptable behaviors.

Training in assertiveness techniques and skills ("I" statements, eye contact, appropriate voice control and volume) are practiced. Increased focus on enhancing listening skills and interpersonal communication styles are modeled. Through role modeling, appropriate skills in confrontation and conflict resolution, as well as giving and receiving constructive feedback are practiced. Direct instruction, modeling and social reinforcement are utilized to enhance appropriate social group interaction. Minor impolite gestures such as belching, burping, and noise making are all addressed in treatment and evaluated for social appropriateness. The facilitators are active during this process, addressing inappropriate behaviors directly, firmly but humanely while remaining respectful to the members.

In the course of treatment, the group members' conflicts in male-female relationships emerge, manifesting themselves through withdrawal or bravado. Members share their anxieties in social situations, exploring feelings of insecurity and in being "found out" (cognitive limitations), or if their disabilities are physical, they express fears of rejection. Issues of low self-esteem present themselves and personal defense mechanisms that may be repulsive to others are addressed and explored by the group members.

EXAMPLE: John

John initially came to the group sassy and provocative with his verbalizations and gestures (eye-winking). He was confronted with his behaviors as being obnoxious and distasteful, encouraging rejection rather than contact. It was suggested through role modeling that a firm handshake, eye contact, and a strong hello replace the old behavior. It took John several weeks to feel secure and overcome his shyness. He explained he used his bravado to counteract his feelings of being short and physically deformed. Through practice and supportive reinforcement by group members, his lewd staring and sexual verbalizations discontinued.

Very often sexually lewd, inappropriate behaviors (verbal and gestural) are a cover up to mask the inadequacies persons with developmental disabilities experience internally. This internal anxiety needs to be directly dealt with and replaced with socially appropriate behaviors which can lead to more socially appropriate interactions.

The purpose of social skill training is to better provide the client with a set of behaviors that will enhance his/her ability to encourage positive, reinforcing relationships, so that the use of force and coercion is not necessary for human contact.

Stage II of Treatment also includes Cognitive Restructuring/Relapse Prevention. In Cognitive Restructuring, focused feedback is used in the interactions among the group members and becomes part of the interpersonal communication style. Clients continue to explore their self-destructive cycles and their perceptual distortions. This phase addresses their emerging sense of depression and loss, their alienation and rejection of peers as an expression of their own self-hate. Through self-examination and feedback the goal is to explore perceptual distortions and self-destructive styles, increase awareness and accept responsibility for one's own sexual behavior.

Through Cognitive Restructuring, the group begins to break into each client's faulty belief system. Their denial of irresponsible sexual and non-sexual behaviors is confronted. They are encouraged to discuss behaviors and incidents more extensively so that distortions will be more visible and can therefore be challenged. Through this sensitive process, clients will begin to identify emotional and attitudinal precipitants to sexually offensive behaviors. They develop an increased awareness of their own emotional and psychological processes that led to their victimizing others. They slowly begin to have an understanding of the impact of their sexual abuse on others, given the exploration of their own sexual abuse and exploitation. Clients have some awareness of emotional and attitudinal precipitants of sexual offending behavior that are unique to a mentally retarded person.

This process is a sensitive and emotional process for the members and facilitators. The facilitator is active, direct and empathetic. By this time, peers can assist in pointing out distorted thinking and have better reality testing. The group facilitator can utilize the members to direct self-evaluation and observe offending behaviors.

Generally, this stage of treatment can be overpowered by expressions of rage in clients being confronted with irresponsible behaviors, as well as severe depression in clients accepting their dual disability of being not only cognitively impaired, but sexually deviant. This acceptance of self is often riddled with self-hate which may be manifested in suicidal ideations, gestures or attempts.

The co-facilitators must be engaging, firm and empathetic to the painstaking efforts the clients make in this phase of treatment. Treatment has often been termed "Tough and Tender," or Salvatore Minuchin's method of "A Kick and a Hug". The emotional aspects of treatment involve managing the client's feelings of depression, loss, anxiety and rejection. As the client passes through this growth cycle, he/she can enter into self-examination and a new yearning for continued treatment. In the process of Relapse Prevention, members review patterns of abusive behaviors and replace it with patterns of coping behaviors and strategies which avoid relapse.

Haaven (1993) simplifies the process of Relapse Prevention by teaching group members to identify and label "set-up" (thoughts/feelings/actions) and replace them with "What to Do's" (coping strategies) that intervene in destructive patterns of behavior.

Stage III

The final stage of treatment is Stage III that involves Transition Planning/Termination/After Care. During this stage of treatment the client has identified coping strategies, recognized safety cues, recognized and overcome distortions, accepted dependency issues and utilized supportive peer interactions in a positive way. The ability to accept one's dual diagnosis and commitment to manage it through the participation in the treatment process becomes the focus of the program with regard to After Care. The prevention of any relapse is an integral part of the transitional planning process in the group.

As members move into this Stage of treatment, they are accompanied by fears, dependency, and hopefulness. Members are able to have an increased ability to bond with peers and leaders. They use the group to work through daily life issues and integrate behavior vulnerabilities to avoid relapse. They have increased awareness of safety cues necessary for not acting out. They rely less on external indicators (supervision) and spontaneously recognize "dangerous" environments. They have an increased awareness of their own distortions and can recognize other members distortions and realities. They are better able to apply coping strategies to situations where their cycle of destructive behavior can begin again. They are better able to accept responsibility for their actions.

One of the goals of group is to recognize that sexual deviant behavior cannot be "cured". Participants need to accept their disabilities and manage them. Accepting the need for on-going therapeutic support and treatment is an indicator of continuing the goal of self-actualization.

Summary

We have learned that a developmentally disabled person who exhibits violent sexual behaviors is capable of being involved in straight forward comprehensive treatment once the sexual disorder is identified. The treatment needs to address the cognitive limitations of the person as well as the underlying emotional issues. Throughout this chapter we have focused on some of the cognitive modules presented in treatment and how psychotherapeutic group process enables the client to integrate the educational/behavioral material. Further studies and basic research will provide better insight into how we can best refine our treatment of this complex disorder.

References

Abel, G., & Becker, M. (1984). *Treatment of child molesters.* Los Angeles: University of California Press.

Becker, J., & Hunter, J. (1993). Aggressive sex offenders. *Child and Adolescent Psychiatric Clinics of North America, 2*, 477-485.

Benson, B., Rice, C., & Meranti. S.V. (1986). Effects of anger management training with adults in group treatment. *Journal of Consult and Clinical Psychology, 154*, 728-729.

Cox-Lindenbaum, D., & Lindenbaum, L. (1994). A modality for treating aggressive behaviors and sexual disorders in people with mental retardation. In N. Bouras (Ed.), *Mental health in mental retardation.* Cambridge: University Press.

Day, K. (1997). Clinical features and offense behavior of mentally retarded sex offenders: A review of research, *NADD Newsletter, 14*, 6. Kingston NY: NADD Press.

Dosen, A. (1997). Proceedings from the NADD International Congress (pp. 3-10). Kingston, NY: NADD Press

Garbarino. (1988). *Sexually abused children in foster care.* Nebraska: Boys Town Press.

Groth, N.A. (1979). Sexual trauma in the life histories and child molestation victimology. *National Journal, 41*, 10-16.

Groth, Nicholas. (1979). *Men who rape.* New York: Plenum Press.

Haaven, J. (1993). *An introduction to the treatment of intellectually disabled sex offender.* Brandon, VT: Safer Society Press.

Haaven, J., Little, R., & Petre-Miller. (1990). *Treating intellectually disabled sex offenders.* Orwell, VT: Safer Society Press.

Kahn, T. (1990). *Pathways.* Orwell VT: Safer Society Press.

Kohut, H. (1994). *Self deficits and addition: The dynamics and treatment of alcoholism, essential papers* (p. 344). Northvale, NJ: Jason Aronson.

National Council of Juvenile and Family Court Judges (1988). *Juvenile and Family Court Journal, 39,*2.

Szymanski, L., & Tanguay, M. (1980). *Emotional disorders of mentally retarded persons.* Baltimore: University Park Press.

CHAPTER TEN

BIBLIOGRAPHY ON COUNSELING AND PSYCHOTHERAPY WITH PERSONS WITH MENTAL RETARDATION

Compiled by:
Robert J. Fletcher, D.S.W., A.C.S.W.
Anne DesNoyers Hurley, Ph.D.
Christine Bellordre

Chapter 10 includes all references to previous chapters as well as references from the NADD publication "Bibliography on Counseling and Psychotherapy".

Abbott, D., & Meredith, W. (1986). Strengths of parents with retarded children. *Family Relations, 35*, 371-375.

Abel, G., & Becker, M. (1984). *Treatment of child molesters.* Los Angeles: University of California Press.

Abel, T. M. (1953). Resistances and difficulties in psychotherapy of mental retardates. *Journal of Clinical Psychology, 9*, 152-156,

Alabiso, F. (1975). Operant control of attentional behavior: A treatment for hyperactivity. *Behavior Therapy, 6,* 39-42.

Albini, J. L., & Dinitz. S. (1965). Psychotherapy with disturbed and defective children: An evaluation of changes in behavior and attitudes. *American Journal of Mental Deficiency, 69,* 560-567

Altman, N. (1995). *The analyst in the inner city: Race, class, and culture through a psychoanalytic lens.* Hillsdale, NJ: Analytic Press.

Aman, M.G. (1991). *Assessing psychopathology and behavior problems in persons with mental retardation: A review of available instruments*. Rockville, MD: US Department of Health and Human Services.

Anderson, J.E. (1968). Group therapy with brain-damaged children. *Hospital and Community Psychiatry, 19,* 175-176.

Andreasen, N.C., & Noyes R. (1975). Suicide attempted by self-immolation. *American Journal of Psychiatry*, 132-135.

Arnatzen, E., & Almas, I. K. (1997). Reduction of phobic behavior for animals in a boy with mental retardation. *Scandinavian Journal of Behavior Therapy, 26*, 124-131.

Asch, A., & Fine, M. (Eds.) (1988). Moving disability beyond stigma. [Special issue]. *Journal of Social Issues, 44* (1).

Astrachan, M. (1955). Group psychotherapy with mentally retarded female adolescents and adults. *American Journal of Mental Deficiency, 61,* 152-156.

Baran, F.N. (1970). Group therapy improves mental retardates' behavior. *Hospital and Community Psychiatry, 23,* 7-11.

Baum, N . T. (1990). Therapy for people with dual diagnosis: Treating the behaviors or the whole person? In A. Dosen, A. van Gennep, & G. J. Zwanikken (Eds.), *Treatment of mental illness and behavioral disorders in the mentally retarded* (pp.143-155). Leiden, The Netherlands: Logon.

Beck, H.L. (1962). Casework with parents of mentally retarded children. *American Journal of Orthopsychiatry 32,* 870-877.

Beck, A.T., Rush, A.J., Shaw, B.F., & Emery, G. (1979). *Cognitive therapy of depression*. New York: Guilford Press.

Becker, J., & Hunter, J. (1993). Aggressive sex offenders. *Child and Adolescent Psychiatric Clinics of North America 2*, 477-485.

Bellack, A. S., & Hersen, M. (Eds.). (1993). *Handbook of behavior therapy in the psychiatric setting*. New York: Plenum.

Benson, B. A. (1995). Problem solving skills training. *The Habilitative Mental Healthcare Newsletter, 14,* 13-15.

Benson, B. A. (1992). *Teaching anger management to persons with mental retardation*. Worthington, OH: International Diagnostic Systems.

Benson, B. A. (1990). Behavioral treatment of depression. In A. Dosen & F.J. Menolascino (Eds.), *Depression in mentally retarded children and adults* (pp. 309-330). Leiden, The Netherlands: Logon.

Benson, B. A. (1986). Anger management training. *Psychiatric Aspects of Mental Retardation Reviews, 5,* 51-55.

Benson, B.A., & Laman, D.S. (1988). Suicidal tendencies of mentally retarded adults in community settings. *Australia and New Zealand Journal of Developmental Disabilities, 14,* 49-54.

Benson, B. A., Rice, C. J., & Miranti, S. V. (1986). Effects of anger management training with mentally retarded adults in group treatment. *Journal of Consulting and Clinical Psychology, 54,* 728-729.

Benson, B.A., Reiss, S., Smith, D.C., & Laman, D.S. (1985). Psychosocial correlates of depression in mentally retarded adults: II. Poor social skills. *American Journal of Mental Deficiency, 89*, 657-659.

Bernfield, G.A., & Jung C.H. (1990). Group therapy with dually diagnosed adolescents. *Group, 14,* 89-98.

Bernstein, N. (1985). Psychotherapy and the retarded adolescent. *Adolescent Psychiatry, 12,* 406-413.

Bernstein, N.R. (1970). *Diminished people: Problems and care of the mentally retarded.* Boston: Little Brown.

Bialer, I. (1967). Psychotherapy and other adjustment techniques with the mentally retarded . In A. A. Baumeister (Ed.), *Mental retardation* (pp. 110-116). Chicago: Aldine.

Bijou, S. W. (1972). Behavior modification in teaching the retarded child. In C.E. Thoresen (Ed.), *The seventy-second yearbook of the national society for the study of education, Part I-Behavior modification in education* (pp. 115-136). Chicago: University of Chicago Press.

Bion, W. (1959). Attacks on linking. *International Journal of Psychoanalysis, 40*, 308-315.

Bird, F., Dores, P. A., Moniz, D., & Robinson, J. (1989). Reducing severe aggressive and self-injurious behaviors with functional communication training. *American Journal of Mental Retardation, 94,* 37-48.

Birenbaum, A. (1971). The mentally retarded child in the home and the family cycle. *Journal of Health and Social Behavior, 12*, 55-65.

Blatner, A. (1996). *Acting-in*(2nd Ed.). New York: Springer.

Blatner, A. (1988). *Foundations of psychodrama history, theory & practice.* New York: Springer.

Bloch, S., & Crouch E. (1985). *Therapeutic factors in group psychotherapy.* New York: Oxford University Press.

Blotzer, M. A., & Ruth, R. (1995). *Sometimes you just want to feel like a human being: Case studies of empowering psychotherapy with people with disabilities*. Baltimore: Paul H. Brookes.

Bojanin, S., & Ispanovic-Radojkovic, V. (1990). Treatment of depression in mentally retarded children: A developmental approach. In A. Dosen & F.J. Menolascino (Eds.), *Depression in mentally retarded children and adults* (pp. 265-280). Leiden, The Netherlands: Logon.

Bregman, S. (1985). Assertiveness training for mentally retarded adults. *Psychiatric Aspects of Mental Retardation Reviews, 4,* 43-48.

Brent, B., & Kolko, D. (1990). Suicide and suicidal behavior in children and adolescents. *Psychiatric Disorders in Children and Adolescents,* 372-391.

Bristol, M., & Schopler, E. (1984). A developmental perspective on stress and coping in families of autistic children. In J. Blacher (Ed.), *Families of severely handicapped children.* New York: Academic Press.

Butler, A., & Elnig, K. (1963). An appraisal of psychotherapy with retarded young adults. *American Journal of Mental Deficiency, 67,* 895-898.

Carlson, G.A., Asarnow, J.R., & Orbach, I. (1994). Developmental aspects of suicidal behavior in children and developmentally delayed adolescents. *New Direction for Children,* 93-107.

Carr, E.G, Levin, L., McConnachie, G., Carlson, J.I., Kemp, D.C., & Smith, C.E. (1994). *Communication-based intervention for problem behavior: A user's guide for producing positive change.* Baltimore: Paul H. Brookes.

Castles, E.E., & Glass. C.R. (1986). Training in social and interpersonal problem-solving skills for mildly and moderately mentally retarded adults. *American Journal of Mental Retardation, 9,* 35-42.

Caton, J. (1990). Symbolic interactional therapy: A treatment intervention for depression in adults with mental retardation. In A. Dosen & F.J. Menolascino (Eds.), *Depression in mentally retarded children and adults* (pp.295-308). Leiden. The Netherlands: Logon.

Caton, J. (1988). Symbolic interaction therapy: A treatment intervention for the mentally retarded adult. *Psychiatric Aspects of Mental Retardation Reviews, 7,* 7-12.

Cautela, J., & Groden, J. (1978). *Relaxation: A comprehensive manual for adults, children, and children with special needs.* Champaign, IL: Research Press.

Chess, S. (1962). Psychiatric treatment of the mentally retarded child with behavior problems. *American Journal of Orthopsychiatry, 32,* 863-869.

Childester, L. (1934). Therapeutic results with mentally retarded children. *American Journal of Orthopsychiatry, 4,* 464-472.

Childester, L., & Menninger, K.A . (1936). The application psychoanalytic methods to the study of mental retardation. *American Journal of Orthopsychiatry, 6,* 616-625.

Ciompi, L. (1976). Late suicide in former mental patients. *Psychiatric Clinical, 1,* 59-63.

Cipani, E. (Ed.). (1989). *The treatment of severe behavior disorders.* Washington, DC: American Association on Mental Retardation.

Cole, C .L., & Gardner, W.I . (1984). Self-management training. *Psychiatric Aspects of Mental Retardation Reviews, 3,* 17-20.

Cole, C. L., Gardner, W. I., & Karan, O. C. (1985). Self-management training of mentally retarded adults presenting severe conduct difficulties. *Applied Research in Mental Retardation, 6,* 337-347.

Cotzin, M. (1948). Group psychotherapy with mentally defective problem boys. *American Journal of Mental Deficiency, 53,* 268-288.

Cox-Lindenbaum, D., & Lindenbaum, L. (1994). A modality for treating aggressive behaviors and sexual disorders in people with mental retardation. In N. Bouras (Ed.), *Mental health in mental retardation.* Cambridge: University Press.

Craighead, L. W., Craighead, W. E., Kazdin, A. E., & Mahoney, M. J. (1994). *Cognitive and behavioral interventions.* Needham Heights, MA: Allyn & Bacon.

Day, K. (1997). Clinical features and offense behavior of mentally retarded sex offenders: *A Review of Research, NADD Newsletter, 14,* 6. Kingston NY: NADD Press.

Demetral, G.D. (1994). A training methodology for establishing reliable self-monitoring with the sex offender who is developmentally disabled. *The Habilitative Mental Healthcare Newsletter 13,* 57-60.

Deutsche, H. (1989). Stress, psychological defense mechanisms, and the private world of the mentally retarded: Applying psychotherapeutic concepts to habilitation. *Psychiatric Aspects of Mental Retardation Reviews. 8,* 27-29.

Deutsche, H. (1985). Grief counseling with the mentally retarded client. *Psychiatric Aspects of Mental Retardation Reviews, 4,* 17-20.

Devevensky, J.L. (1979). Children's fears: A developmental comparison of normal and exceptional children. *Journal of Genetic Psychology, 135,* 11-21.

Dosen, A. (1993). Part 1: Overview. In R. Fletcher & A. Dosen (Eds.), *Mental health aspects of mental retardation* (pp. 3-17). New York: Lexington Books.

Dosen, A. (1997). Proceedings from the NADD International Congress (pp. 3-10). Kingston, NY: NADD Press.

Dosen, A. (1990). Developmental-dynamic relationship therapy. In A. Dosen, A. van Gennep, & G. Zwanikken (Eds.), *Treatment of mental illness and behavioral disorders in the mentally retarded* (pp. 37-44). Leiden, The Netherlands: Logon.

Dosen, A. (1990). Psychotherapeutic approaches in the treatment of depressive mentally retarded children. In A. Dosen & F.J. Menolascino (Eds.), *Depression in mentally retarded children and adults* (pp. 255-264). Leiden, The Netherlands: Logon.

Dossick, J., & Shea, E. (1990). *Creative therapy II: 50 more exercises for groups.* Sarasota, FL: Professional Resource Exchange.

Dubros, S. G., & Daniels, G. J. (1966). An experimental approach to the reduction of overactive behavior. *Behavior Research and Therapy, 4,* 251-258.

Durand, M., & Crimmins, D. (1992). *The motivation assessment scale (MAS) administration guide.* Topeka, KS: Monoco.

Durand, V. M. (1990). *Severe behavior problems: A functional communication training approach.* New York: Guilford.

Erfanian, N., & Miltenberger, R. G. (1990). Brief report: Contact desensitization in the treatment of dog phobias in persons who have mental retardation. *Behavioral Residential Treatment, 5,* 55-60.

Fawcett, J., Clark, D., & Scheftner, W. (1991). The assessment and management of the suicidal patient. *Psychiatric Medicine, 9,* 299-310.

Feldman, F. (1946). Psychoneuroses in the mentally retarded. *American Journal of Mental Deficiency, 51,* 247-253.

Ferguson, P.M., Ferguson, D.L., & Jones, D. (1988). Generations of hope: Parental perspectives on the transitions of their children with severe retardation from school to adult life. *Journal of the Association for Persons with Severe Handicaps, 13,* 177-187.

Fine, M.J. (1969). Counseling with the educable mentally retarded. *Training School Bulletin, 66,* 105-110.

Fine, R.H., & Dawson, J.C . (1964). A therapy program for the mildly retarded adolescent. *American Journal of Mental Deficiency, 69,* 23.

Fisher, L.A., & Wolfson, I.N. (1953). Group therapy of mental defectives. *American Journal of Mental Deficiency, 57,* 463-476.

Flavell, J. E. (1982). The treatment of self-injurious behavior. *Behavior Therapy, 13,* 529-554.

Fletcher, R. (1984). Group therapy with mentally retarded persons with emotional disorders. *Psychiatric Aspects of Mental Retardation Reviews, 3,* 21-24.

Fletcher, R., & Menolascino, F. (1989). *Mental retardation and mental illness. Assessment, treatment, and service for the dually diagnosed.* New York: Lexington Books.

Fletcher, R.J. (1993). Individual psychotherapy for persons with mental retardation. In R.J. Fletcher & A. Dosen (Eds.), *Mental health aspects of mental retardation: Progress in assessment and treatment* (pp. 327-349). New York: Lexington Books.

Fletcher, R. J., & Dosen, A. (1993). *Mental health aspects of mental retardation: Progress in assessment and treatment.* New York : Lexington Books.

Floyd, F.J., Singer, G.H.S., Powers, L.E., & Costigan, C.L. (1996). Families coping with mental retardation: Assessment and therapy. In J.W.Jacobson & J.A. Mullick (Eds.), *Manual of diagnosis and professional practice in mental retardation* (pp. 355-370). Washington, DC: American Psychological Association.

Foxx, R.M., & Bittlel, R.G. (1989). *Thinking it through: Teaching problem solving strategy for community living.* Champaign IL: Research Press.

Foxx, R. M., McMorrow, M. J., & Schloss, C. N. (1983). Stacking the deck: Teaching social skills to retarded adults with a modified table game. *Journal of Applied Behavior Analysis, 16,* 157-170.

Frame, C., Matson J.L., Sonis W.A., Fialkov M.J., & Kazdin, A.E. (1982). Behavioral treatment of depression in a prepubertal child. *Journal of Behavior Therapy and Experimental Psychiatry, 13*, 239-243.

Freeman, B.J., Roy, R.R., & Hemmick, S. (1976). Extinction of a phobia of physical examinations in a seven-year-old mentally retarded boy: A case study. *Behavior Research and Therapy, 14,* 63-64.

Fresco, T., Philbin, L., & Petus, K. (1993). Sexual assault support groups for women with developmental disabilities. *The Habilitative Mental Healthcare Newsletter, 12,* 98-103.

Freud, S. (1916-1917/1965). *Introductory lectures on psychoanalysis.* (Standard eds. 15, 16). London: Hogarth.

Friesen, W.V., & Ekman, P. (1976). *Pictures of facial affect.* Palo Alto, CA: Consulting Psychologists Press.

Gaedt, C. (1995). Psychotherapeutic approaches in the treatment of mental illness and behavioral disorders in mentally retarded people: The significance of a psychoanalytic perspective. *Journal of Intellectual Disability Research 39*, 233-239.

Gallagher, J.J., Beckman, P., & Cross, A. H. (1983). Families of handicapped children: Sources of stress and its amelioration. *Exceptional Children, 50*, 10-19.

Garbarino. (1988). *Sexually abused children in foster care.* Nebraska: Boys Town Press.

Gardner, W. I. (1998). Creating preventive and proactive interventions. In D.M. Griffiths, W. I. Gardner, & J. Nugent (Eds.), *Behavior supports: Individual centered interventions* (pp. 77-97). Kingston, NY: NADD Press.

Gardner, W. I. (1996). Nonspecific behavioral symptoms in persons with a dual diagnosis: A psychological model for integrating biomedical and psychosocial diagnoses and interventions. *Psychology in Mental Retardation and Developmental Disabilities, 21,* 6-11.

Gardner, W. I. (1988). Behavior therapies: Past, present, and future. In J. A. Stark, F. J. Menolascino, M. H. Albarelli, & D. Gray (Eds.), *Mental retardation and mental health: Classification, diagnosis, treatment, services* (pp. 161-172). New York: Springer-Verlag.

Gardner, W. I., & Cole, C. L. (1993). Aggression and related conduct disorders: Definition, assessment, treatment. In J. L. Matson & R. P. Barrett (Eds.), *Psychopathology in the mentally retarded* (pp. 213-252). Boston: Allyn & Bacon.

Gardner, W. I., & Cole, C. L. (1989). Self-management approaches. In E. Cipani (Ed.), *The treatment of severe behavior disorders: Behavior analysis approaches* (pp. 19-35). Washington, DC: American Association on Mental Retardation.

Gardner, W.I., & Graeber, J.L. (1990). People with mental retardation and severe behavior disorders: A multimodal behavioral diagnostic and treatment model. *The NADD Newsletter, 7,* 1-2. Kingston, NY: NADD Press.

Gardner, W. I., & Moffatt, C. W. (1990). Aggressive behavior: Definition, assessment, treatment. *International Review of Psychiatry, 2,* 91-100.

Gardner, W. I., & Sovner, R. (1994). *Self-injurious behaviors: Diagnosis and treatment.* Willow Street, PA: Vida.

Gardner, W. I., & Whalen, J. P. (1996). A multi-modal behavior analytic model for evaluating the effects of medical problems on nonspecific behavioral symptoms in persons with developmental disabilities. *Behavioral Interventions: Theory and Practice in Residential and Community-Based Clinical Programs, 11*, 147-161.

Gardner, W. I., Clees, T., & Cole, C. L. (1983). Self-management of disruptive verbal ruminations by a mentally retarded adult. *Applied Research in Mental Retardation, 4,* 41-58.

Gardner, W. I., Graeber, J. L., & Cole, C. L. (1996). Behavior therapies: A multimodal diagnostic and intervention model. In J. W. Jacobson & J. A. Mulick (Eds.), *Manual of diagnosis and professional practice in mental retardation* (pp. 355-370). Washington, DC: American Psychological Association.

Gilligan, C. (1982). *In a different voice.* Cambridge: Harvard University Press.

Gilson, S.F., & Levitas, A.S. (1987). Psychosocial crisis with the mentally retarded client. *Psychiatric Aspects of Mental Retardation Reviews, 6,* 27-31.

Gilson, S.F., Baskind, F., & Bricout, J. (1998). Social work's perspective on disability and our reality: Families and society. *Journal of Contemporary Human Services, 79,* 188-196.

Glassman, L.A. (1943). Is dull normal intelligence a contraindication for psychotherapy? *Smith College Studies in Social Work, 13,* 275-298.

Godschalx, S.M. (1983). Mark: Psychotherapy with a developmentally disabled adult. *Journal of Nursing Scholarship, 5,* 12-15.

Gorlow, L., Butler, A., Einig, K.K.G., & Smith, J.A. (1963). An appraisal of self-attitudes and behavior following group psychotherapy with retarded young adults. *American Journal of Mental Deficiency, 57,* 893-898.

Gould, M., Fisher, P., Parides, M., Flory, M., & Shaffer, D. (1996). Psychosocial risk factors of child and adolescent completed suicide archives. *General Psychiatry, 53,* 1155-1162.

Greenberger, D., & Pedesky, C. (1995). *Mind over mood: A cognitive therapy treatment manual for clients.* New York: Guilford Press.

Griffiths, D. (1990). Teaching social competency Part 1. Practical guidelines. *The Habilitative Mental Healthcare Newsletter, 9,* 1-5.

Griffiths, D. (1990). Teaching social competency Part 2. The social life game. *The Habilitative Mental Healthcare Newsletter, 9,* 9-13.

Griffiths, D. M., Feldman, M. A., & Tough, S. (1997). Programming generalization of social skills in adults with developmental disabilities: Effects of generalization and social validity. *Behavior Therapy, 28,* 253-269.

Griffiths, D. M., Gardner, W. I., & Nugent, J. (1998). *Behavioral supports: Individual centered behavioral interventions.* Kingston, NY: NADD Press.

Griffiths, D., Hingsburger, D., & Christian, R. (1985). Treating developmentally handicapped sexual offenders: The York behavior management services treatment program. *Psychiatric Aspects of Mental Retardation Reviews, 4,* 49-52.

Groth, N.A. (1979). Sexual trauma in the life histories and child molestation victimology. *National Journal, 41,* 10-16.

Groth, Nicholas. (1979). *Men who rape.* New York: Plenum Press.

Guralnik, M. J. (1973). Behavior therapy with an acrophobia mentally retarded young adult. *Journal of Behavior Therapy and Experimental Psychiatry, 4,* 263-265.

Haaven, J. (1993). *An introduction to the treatment of intellectually disabled sex offender.* Brandon, VT: Safer Society Press.

Haaven, J., Little, R., & Petre-Miller. (1990). *Treating intellectually disabled sex offenders.* Orwell, VT: Safer Society Press.

Hahn, H. (1993). The politics of physical differences: Disability and discrimination. In M. Nagler (Ed.), *Perspectives on disability* (2nd ed., pp. 37-42). Palo Alto, CA: Health Markets Research.

Harris, E.C., & Barraclough, B. (1997). Suicide as an outcome for mental disorders meta-analysis. *British Journal of Psychiatry,* 205-228.

Harvey, J.R. (1979). The potential of relaxation training for the mentally retarded. *Mental Retardation, 17,* 71-76.

Hayashino, D.S. Wirtele, S.K., & Klebe, K.H. (1995). Child molesters: An examination of cognitive factors. *Journal of Interpersonal Violence*, 10, 106-116.

Heinemann, E., & De Groef, J. (Eds.). (1997). *Psychoanalyse und geistige Behinderung.* Mainz: Matthias Grunewald-Verlag .

Heiser, K.F. (1951). Psychotherapy for the mentally retarded child. *The Training School Bulletin, 48,*111-119.

Hellendoorn, J. (1990). Indications and goals for play therapy with the mentally retarded. In A. Dosen, A. van Gennep, & G. J. Zwanikken (Eds.), *Treatment of mental illness and behavioral disorders in the mentally retarded* (pp. 179-188). Leiden, The Netherlands: Logon.

Hennicke, K., & Bradl, C. (1990). Systemic family therapy and mental retardation. In A. Dosen, A. van Gennep, G.J. Zwanikken (Eds.), *Proceedings of NADD International Congress*. Leiden, The Netherlands: Logon.

Heyman, B., & Huckle, S. (1993). Normal life in a hazardous world: How adults with moderate learning difficulties and their careers cope with risks and dangers. *Disability, Handicap & Society, 8,* 143-160.

Hill, R. (1958). Generic features of families under stress. *Social Casework, 39,* 139-150.

Hingsburger, D. (1989). Relationship training, sexual behavior and persons with developmental handicaps. *Psychiatric Aspects of Mental Retardation Reviews, 8,* 33-37.

Hingsburger, D. (1988). Clients and curriculum: Preparing for sex education. *Psychiatric Aspects of Mental Retardation Reviews, 7,* 13-18.

Hingsburger, D. (1987). Sex counseling with the developmentally handicapped: The assessment and management of seven critical problems. *Psychiatric Aspects of Mental Retardation Reviews, 6,* 41-46.

Hiss, H., & Kozak, M. J. (1991). Exposure treatment of obsessive-compulsive disorders in the mentally retarded. *The Behavior Therapist, 14,* 163-167.

Holding, T.A., & Barraclough, B.M. (1975). Psychiatric morbidity in a sample of a London coroner's open verdicts. *British Journal of Psychiatry,* 133-43.

Hollins, D. (1995). Managing grief better: People with developmental disabilities. *The Habilitative Mental Healthcare Newsletter, 14,* 50-52.

Hollins, D., & Sireling, L. (1990). *Working through loss with people who have learning disabilities.* Windsor, UK: NFER-Nelson.

Hollins, D., Sireling, L., & Webb, B. (1992). *When mum died, when dad died (for people with learning disabilities).* London: Sovereign Press.

Hollins, S. (1995). Managing grief better: People with developmental disabilities. *The Habilitative Mental Healthcare Newsletter, 14*, 50-52.

Hollins, S., Sinason, V., & Thompson, S. (1994). Individual, group and family psychotherapy. In N. Bouras (Ed.), *Mental health in mental retardation : Recent advances and practices,* (pp. 233-243). Cambridge: University Press.

Horner, R. H., & Day, H. M. (1991). The effects of response efficiency on functionally equivalent competing behaviors. *Journal of Applied Behavior Analysis, 24,* 719-732.

Howell, J.R. (1957). Casework with retarded children in an institutional setting. *American Journal of Mental Deficiency, 61,* 592-598.

Hurley, A.D. (1996). Vocational rehabilitation counseling approaches to support adults with mental retardation. *The Habilitative Mental Healthcare Newsletter, 15,* 30-35.

Hurley, A.D. (1989). Individual psychotherapy with mentally retarded individuals: A review and call for research. *Research in Developmental Disabilities, 10*, 261-275.

Hurley, A.D. (1989). Behavior therapy for psychiatric disorders in mentally retarded individuals. In R. Fletcher & F.J. Menolascino (Eds.), *Mental retardation and mental illness* (pp.127-140). Lexington, MA: Lexington Books.

Hurley, A.D . (1984). Diagnosis and treatment of compulsive behaviors in mentally retarded persons. *Psychiatric Aspects of Mental Retardation, 3,* 37-40.

Hurley, A.D., & Bellordre, C. (1996). *Bibliography on counseling and psychotherapy.* Kingston, NY: NADD Press.

Hurley, A.D., & Hurley, F.J. (1993). Providing services to families of persons with developmental disabilities. *The Habilitative Mental Healthcare Newsletter, 12,* 47-52.

Hurley, A.D., & Hurley, F.J. (1987). Counseling and psychotherapy with mentally retarded clients: II. Establishing a relationship. *Psychiatric Aspects of Mental Retardation Reviews, 6*, 15-20.

Hurley, A., & Hurley F. J. (1987). Working with the parents of handicapped children. *Psychiatric Aspects of Mental Retardation Reviews, 6,* 53-57.

Hurley, A.D., & Hurley, F.J.(1986). Counseling and psychotherapy with mentally retarded clients: I. The initial interview. *Psychiatric Aspects of Mental Retardation Reviews, 5*, 22-26.

Hurley, A. D., & Silka, V. R. (1998). Cognitive-behavioral treatment for panic disorder. *Mental Health Aspects of Developmental Disabilities, 1,* 119-123.

Hurley, A.D., & Sovner, R. (1991). Cognitive behavioral therapy for depression in individuals with developmental disabilities. *The Habilitative Mental Healthcare Newsletter, 10,* 41-47.

Hurley, A.D., & Sovner, R. (1985). Paradoxical interventions with mentally retarded clients. *Psychiatric Aspects of Mental Retardation Reviews, 4,* 39-42.

Hurley, A.D., & Sovner, R. (1983). Phobic behavior in mentally retarded persons. *Psychiatric Aspects of Mental Retardation Reviews, 2,* 13-15.

Hurley, A., Pfadt, A., Tomasulo, D., & Gardner, W. (1996). Counseling and psychotherapy. In J. Jacobson & J. Mulick (Eds.), *Manual of diagnosis and professional practice in mental retardation* (pp. 371-380). Washington, DC: American Psychological Association.

Jackson, H. J. (1983). Current trends in the treatment of phobias in autistic and mentally retarded persons. *Australia and New Zealand Journal of Developmental Disabilities, 9,* 191-208.

Jackson, H. J., & Hooper J. P. (1981). Some issues arising from the desensitization of a dog phobia in a mildly retarded female: Or should we take the bite out of the bark? *Australian Journal of Developmental Disabilities, 7,* 9-16.

Jackson, H. J., & King, N. J. (1982). The therapeutic management of an autistic child's phobia using laughter as the anxiety inhibitor. *Behavioral Psychotherapy, 10,* 364-369.

Jackson, T. L., & Altman, R. (1996). Self-management of aggression in an adult male with mental retardation and severe behavior disorders. *Education and Training in Mental Retardation and Developmental Disabilities, 30,* 55-65.

Jacobson, J.W. (1982). Problem behavior and psychiatric impairment within a developmentally disabled population I: Behavior frequency. *Applied Research in Mental Retardation, 3,* 121-139.

Jacobson, J. W., & Mulick, J. J. (Eds.). (1996). *Manual of diagnosis and professional practice in mental retardation.* Washington, DC: American Psychological Association.

Jageman, L. W., & Myers, J.E. (1988). A conceptual model for counseling adult mentally retarded persons. *Journal of Applied Rehabilitation Counseling, 18,* 17-21.

Jakab, I. (1982). Psychiatric disorders in mental retardation: Recognition, diagnosis, and treatment. In I. Jakab (Ed.), *Mental retardation* (pp. 270-322). New York: Kargan.

Jakab, I. (1970). Psychotherapy of the mentally retarded child. In M. R. Bernstein, (Ed.), *Diminished people (pp.* 223-263). Boston: Little/Brown.

Jakab, I . (1969) . Art therapy with a 12 year old girl who witnessed suicide. *Psychotherapy & Psychosomatics, 17,* 309-324.

James, I.A. (1995). Helping people with learning disability to cope with bereavement. *British Journal of Learning Disabilities, 23,* 74-78.

Jones, R.B.P., Miller, B., Williams, H., & Goldthorp, J. (1997). Theoretical and practical issues in cognitive-behavioral approaches for people with learning disabilities: A radical behavioral approach. In Kroese, Dagnan, & Loumidis (Eds.), *Cognitive-behavior therapy for people with learning disabilities.* New York: Routledge.

Josephs, L. (1995). *Balancing empathy and interpretation.* Northvale, NJ: Jason Aronson.

Kahn, T. (1990). *Pathways.* Orwell, VT: Safer Society Press.

Kaldeck, R. (1958). Group psychotherapy with mentally defective adolescents and adults. *International Journal of Group Psychotherapy, 8,* 185-192.

Kaplan, H.I., Sadock, B.J., & Grebb, J.A. (1994). Kaplan and Sadock's synopsis of psychiatry behavioral sciences clinical psychiatry (7th ed.). Baltimore: Williams and Wilkins.

Kelly, J.A,. & Christoff, K. (1985). Job interview training. *Psychiatric Aspects of Mental Retardation Reviews, 4,* 5-8.

Koegel, L. K., Koegel, R. L., & Parks, D. R. (1990). *How to teach self-management to people with severe disabilities: A training manual.* Washington, DC: U.S. Department of Education, Office of Educational Research and Improvement, Educational Resources Information Center.

Kohut, H. (1994). *Self deficits and addition: The dynamics and treatment of alcoholism, essential papers* (p. 344). Northvale, NJ: Jason Aranson.

Kroese, B.S. (1997). Cognitive-behavior therapy for people with learning disabilities: Conceptual and contextual issues. In Kroese, Dagnan, & Loumidis (Eds.), *Cognitive-behavior therapy for people with learning disabilities.* New York: Routledge.

Landau, M.E. (1968). Group psychotherapy with deaf retardates. *International Journal of Psychotherapy, 18,* 345-351.

Lansdell, C. (1990). Psychotherapy with persons who have developmental disabilities: A bio-psychosocial model. *The NADD Newsletter, 7,* 1-5. Kingston, NY: NADD Press.

Leland, H., & Smith, E. D. (1965). *Play therapy with mentally subnormal children.* New York: Grune & Stratton.

Leland, H., & Smith, E. D. (1962). Unstructured material in play therapy for emotionally disturbed, brain damaged, mentally retarded children. *American Journal of Mental Deficiency, 66,* 621-628.

Levey, S., & Howells, K. (1991). Anger and its management. *Journal of Forensic Psychiatry, 1,* 305-327.

Levitas, A.S, & Gilson, S.F. (1997). Individual psychotherapy for persons with mild and moderate mental retardation. *The NADD Newsletter, 13,* 4. Kingston, NY: NADD Press.

Levitas, A.S., & Gilson, S.F. (1994). Psychosocial development of children and adolescents with mild and moderate mental retardation. In N. Bouras (Ed.), *Mental health in mental retardation: Recent advances and practices* (pp. 34-45). Cambridge: University Press.

Levitas, A.S., & Gilson, S.F. (1990). Toward the developmental understanding of the impact of mental retardation on assessment of psychopathology. In E. Dibble & D.G. Gray (Eds.), *Assessment of behavior problems in persons with mental retardation living in the community* (pp. 71-106). Rockville, MD: National Institute of Mental Health.

Levitas, A.S., & Gilson, S.F. (1989). Psychodynamic psychotherapy with mildly and moderately retarded patients. In R Fletcher & F. Menolascino (Eds.), *Mental retardation and mental illness: Assessment, treatment and service for the dually diagnosed* (pp. 71-109). Lexington, MA: Lexington Books.

Levitas, A., & Gilson, S. (1987). Transference, countertransference, and resistance. The *NADD Newsletter, 1,* 2-7. Kingston, NY: NADD Press.

Levitas, A. S., & Gilson, S .F. (1987). Psychosocial crises in the lives of mentally retarded people. *Psychiatric Aspects of Mental Retardation Reviews, 6,* 27-31.

Levitas, A., & Gilson, S. (1997). Individual psychotherapy for persons with mild and moderate mental retardation. *The NADD Newsletter, 14,* 34-38. Kingston, NY: NADD Press

Levitas, A., & Gilson, S. (1989). Psychodynamic psychotherapy with mildly and moderately retarded patients. In R. Fletcher & F. Menolacino (Eds.), *Mental retardation and mental illness: Assessment, treatment and service for the dually diagnosed* (pp. 71-109*)*. New York: Lexington Books.

Lezak, M.D. (1996). *Neuropsychological assessment (3rd ed.)* New York: Oxford University Press.

Lindsay, W. R., & Baty, F. J. (1989). Group relaxation training with adults who are mentally handicapped. *Behavioral Psychotherapy, 17,* 43-51.

Lindsay, W. R., Howells, L., & Pitcaithly, D. (1992). Cognitive therapy for depression with individuals with intellectual disabilities. *British Journal of Medical Psychology, 66,* 135-141.

Lindsay, W.R., Baty, F.J., Mitchie, A.M., & Richardson, I. (1989). A comparison of anxiety treatments with adults who have moderate and severe mental retardation. *Research in Developmental Disabilities, 10,* 129-140.

Lindsay, W. R., Marshall, I., Neilson, C., Quinn, K., & Smith, A. H. W. (1998). The treatment of a learning disability convicted of exhibitionism. *Research in Developmental Disabilities, 19,* 295-316.

Linehan, M. (1993) *Cognitive behavioral treatment of borderline personality disorder.* New York: Guilford Press.

Linehan, M. (1993) *Skills training manual for treating borderline personality disorder.* New York: Guilford Press.

Loschen, E., & Osman. (1992). Self-injurious behavior in the developmentally disabled: Assessment techniques. *Psychopharmacology Bulletin, 28,* 433-437.

Lott, G. (1970). Psychotherapy of the mentally retarded: Values and cautions. In F.J. Menolascino (Ed.), *Psychiatric approaches to mental retardation* (pp. 227-250). New York: Basic Books.

Lowe, S.R., Matson, J.L., & West, D. (1990). Mothers as therapists for autistic children's phobias. *Journal of Applied Behavior Analysis, 23,* 379-385.

Lowery, M. A., & Sovner, R. (1991). Severe behavior problems associated with rapid cycling bipolar disorder in two adults with profound mental retardation. *Journal of Intellectual Disability Research, 36,* 269-281.

Lowry, M. (1997). Unmasking mood disorders: Recognizing and measuring symptomatic behaviors. *The Habilitative Mental Healthcare Newsletter, 16.*

Ludwig, A., & Hingsburger, D. (1989). Preparation for counseling and psychotherapy: Teaching about feelings. *Psychiatric Aspects of Mental Retardation Reviews, 8,* 2-7.

Luiselli, J.K. (1977). Case report: An attendant-administered contingency management program for the treatment of toileting phobia. *Journal of Mental Deficiency Research, 21,* 283-288.

Luiselli, J. K., & Cameron, M. J. (Eds.). (1998). *Antecedent control: Innovative approaches to behavioral support.* Baltimore: Paul H. Brookes.

Mansdorf, I. J. (1976). Eliminating fear in a mentally retarded adult by behavioral hierarchies and operant techniques. *Journal of Behavior Therapy and Experimental Psychiatry, 7,* 189-190.

Mansdorf, I. J., & Ben-David, N. (1986). Operant and cognitive intervention to restore effective functioning following a death in a family. *Behavior Therapy and Experimental Psychiatry, 17,* 193-196.

Matson, J. (1992). DASH: *Diagnostic assessment for the severely handicapped.* Oxford, MS: Oxford.

Matson, J. (1988). *The PIRMA manual.* Worthington, OH: International Diagnostics Systems.

Matson, J.L. (1984). Behavioral treatment of psychosomatic complaints in the mentally retarded. *American Journal of Mental Deficiency, 88,* 639-646.

Matson, J.L. (1984). Psychotherapy with persons who are mentally retarded. *Mental Retardation, 22,* 170-175 .

Matson, J.L. (1984). Social skill training. *Psychiatric Aspects of Mental Retardation Reviews, 3,* 1-4.

Matson, J.L. (1982). Treatment of behavioral characteristics of depression in the mentally retarded. *Behavior Therapy, 13,* 209-218.

Matson, J.L. (1981). A controlled outcome study of phobias in mentally retarded adults. *Behavior Research and Therapy, 19,* 101-107.

Matson, J.L. (1981). Assessment and treatment of clinical fears in mentally retarded children. *Journal of Applied Behavior Analysis, 14,* 145-152.

Matson, J. L., & Barrett, R. P. (Eds.). (1993). *Psychopathology in the mentally retarded.* Boston: Allyn & Bacon.

Matson, J.L., & Gardner, W.I. (1991). Behavioral learning theory and current application to severe behavior problems in persons with mental retardation. *Clinical Psychology Review, 11,* 175-183.

Matson, J.L., & Senators, V. (1981). A comparison of traditional psychotherapy and social skills training for improving interpersonal functioning of mentally retarded adults. *Behavior Therapy, 12,* 369-382.

Matson, J. L., & Stephens, R. M. (1978). Increasing appropriate behaviors of explosive chronic psychiatric patients with a social skills training package. *Behavior Modification, 2,* 61-76.

Matson, J.L., Dotting, J., & Senatore V. (1982). Treating depression of a mentally retarded adult. *British Journal of Mental Subnormality, 16,* 86-88.

Meichenbaum, D. (1994). *A clinical handbook/practical therapist manual for assessing and treating adults with post-traumatic stress disorder (PTSD).* Waterloo, Canada: Institute Press.

Meizio, S. (1967). Group therapy with mentally retarded adolescents in institutional settings. *International Journal of Psychotherapy, 17,* 321-327.

Menolascino, E., Lazar, J., & Stark, J. (1989). Diagnosis and management of depression and suicidal behavior in persons with severe mental retardation. *Journal of the Multi-Handicapped Person, 2,* 89-103.

Merighi, J., Edison, M., & Zigler, E. (1990). The role of motivational factors in the functioning of mentally retarded individuals. In R. M. Hodapp, J.A. Burack & E. Zigler (Eds.), *Issues in the developmental approach to mental retardation.* Cambridge: University Press.

Michel-Smith, H., Gottsegen, M., & Gottsegen, G. (1955). A group technique for mental retardates. *International Journal of Group Psychotherapy, 5,* 84-90.

Miller, J. B. (1986). *Toward a new psychology of women.* Boston: Beacon Press.

Milner, C., & Borgen-Jensen, K. (1996). Time limited group therapy for survivors of abuse who have developmental disabilities. *The NADD Newsletter, 13,* 1-6. Kingston, NY: NADD Press.

Minkoff, R.A. (1991). Counseling parents with adult children transitioning into residential programs. *The Habilitative Mental Healthcare Newsletter, 10,* 9-11.

Monfils, M. (1989). Group psychotherapy. In R. Fletcher & F.J. Menolascino (Eds.), *Mental retardation and mental illness: Assessment, treatment, and service for the dually diagnosed* (pp. 111-125). Lexington, MA: Lexington.

Moroney, R. M. (1986). *Shared responsibility: Families and social policy.* New York: Aldine.

Muller, P.J. (1985). Metacognition and attention. *Instructional Practices, 2,* 181-221.

Mundy, L. (1957). Therapy with physically and mentally handicapped children in a mental deficiency hospital. *Journal of Clinical Psychology, 13,* 3-9.

Murray, M. (1970). Needs of parents of mentally retarded children. [Pamphlet]. Arlington, TX: National Association for Retarded Citizens.

Myers, B.A., (1987). Psychiatric problems in adolescents with developmental disabilities. *Journal of the Academy of Child and Adolescent Psychiatry, 26,* 74-79.

National Council of Juvenile and Family Court Judges (1988). *Juvenile and Family Court Journal, 39,* 2.

Nehan, S. (1951). Psychotherapy in relation to mental deficiency. *American Journal of Mental Deficiency, 55,* 557-572 .

Nezu, C. M., & Nezu, A. M. (1995). Clinical decision making in everyday practice: The science in the art. *Cognitive and Behavioral Practice, 2,* 5-25.

Nezu, C.M., & Nezu A.M. (1994). Outpatient psychotherapy for adults with mental retardation and concomitant psychopathology: Research and clinical imperatives. *Journal of Consulting and Clinical Psychology, 62,* 34-42.

Nezu, C.M., Nezu, A.M., & Arean, P. (1991). Assertiveness and problem solving training for mildly mentally retarded persons with dual diagnoses. *Research in Developmental Disabilities, 12,* 371-386.

Nezu, C. M., Nezu, A. M., & Gill-Weiss M. J. (1992). *Psychopathology in persons with mental retardation: Clinical guidelines for assessment and treatment.* Champaign, IL: Research Press.

Nisbet, J., Covert, S., & Schuh, M. (1988). Family involvement in the transition from school to adult life. In F.R. Rusch, L. DeStefano, J. Chadsey-Rusch, L.A. Phelps, & E. Szymanski (Eds.), *Transition from school to adult life: Models, linkages and policy (pp.* 407-424). Sycamore, IL: Sycamore.

Obler, M., & Terwillinger, R. F. (1970). Pilot study on the effectiveness of systematic desensitization with neurologically impaired children with phobic disorders. *Journal of Consulting and Clinical Psychology, 34,* 314-318.

O'Connor, N., & Young, L.A. (1955) . Methods of evaluating the group psychotherapy of unstable defective delinquents. *Journal of Genetic Psychology, 87,* 109-110.

O'Donohue, W. O., & Krasner, L. (Eds.). (1995). *Theories of behavior therapy: Exploring behavior change.* Washington, DC: American Psychological Association.

Olshansky, S. (1962). Chronic sorrow: A response to having a mentally defective child. *Social Casework, 43,* 190-193.

Orr, R.R., Cameron, S.J., Dobson, L.A., & Day, D.M. (1993). Age-related changes in stress experienced by families with a child who has developmental delays. *Mental Retardation: American Association on Mental Retardation, 31,* 171-176.

Paniagua, C. & DeFazio, A. (1989) Psychodynamics of the mildly retarded and borderline-intelligence adult. In R. Fletcher & F. Menolascino (Eds.), *Mental retardation and mental illness: Assessment, treatment and service for the dually diagnosed* (pp. 35-57). New York: Lexington Books.

Paniagua, C., & DeFazio, A. (1983). Psychodynamics of the mildly retarded and borderline intelligence adult. *Psychiatric Quarterly, 55,* 242-252.

Pary, R.J., Strauss, D., & White, J.F. (1997). A population survey of suicide attempts in persons with and without down syndrome. *Down Syndrome Quarterly, 2,* 12-13.

Peck, C.L. (1977). Desensitization for the treatment of fear in the high level adult retardate. *Behavior Research and Therapy, 15,* 137-148.

Pendler, B., & Hingsburger, D. (1990). Sexuality: Dealing with parents. *The Habilitative Mental Healthcare Newsletter, 9,* 29-34. Kingston, NY: NADD Press.

Perkins, D.M. (1993). The use of counseling and psychotherapy with dually diagnosed persons. *The NADD Newsletter, 10,* 1-7. Kingston, NY: NADD Press.

Pfadt, A. (1991). Group psychotherapy with mentally retarded adults: Issues related to design, implementation and evaluation. *Research in Developmental Disabilities, 12,* 261-285.

Pfadt, A. (1990). Diagnosing and treating psychopathology in clients with a dual diagnosis: An integrative model. In A. Dosen, A. van Gennep, & G. J. Zwanikken (Eds.), *Treatment of mental illness and behavioral disorders in the mentally retarded* (pp. 217-224). Leiden, The Netherlands: Logan.

Piazza, C., & Fisher, W.W. (1991). Bedtime fading in the treatment of podiatric insomnia. *Journal of Behavior Therapy and Experimental Psychiatry, 22,* 53-56.

Prouty, G. (1991). Pre-therapy: A treatment for the dual/ diagnosed-schizophrenic/retarded. *The NADD Newsletter, 8,* 1-4. Kingston, NY: NADD Press.

Prouty, G. (1976). Pre-therapy--a method of treating pre-expressive psychotic and retarded patients. Psy*chotherapy: Theory, Research, and Practice, 13,* 290-294.

Prouty, G., & Cronwall, M. (1990). Psychotherapeutic approaches in the treatment of depression in mentally retarded adults. In A. Dosen & F.J. Menolascino (Eds.), *Depression in mentally retarded children and adults* (pp. 281-294). Leiden, The Netherlands: Logon.

Prouty, G., & Kubiak, M.A. (1988). Pre-therapy with mentally retarded/ psychotic clients. *Psychiatric Aspects of Mental Retardation Reviews, 7,* 61-66.

Pyles, D. A., Muniz, K., Cade, A., & Sivla, R. (1997). A behavioral diagnostic paradigm for integrating behavior-analytic and psycho-pharmacological interventions for people with a dual diagnosis. *Research in Developmental Disabilities, 18,* 185-214.

Razza, N., & Tomasulo, D. (1996). The sexual abuse continuum: Therapeutic interventions with individuals with mental retardation. *The Habilitative Mental Healthcare Newsletter, 15,* 19-22.

Razza, N. & Tomasulo, D. (1996). The sexual abuse continuum: Part 2. Therapeutic interventions with individuals with mental retardation. *The Habilitative Mental Healthcare Newsletter, 15,* 84-86.

Razza, N., & Tomasulo, D. (1996). The sexual abuse continuum: Part 3. Therapeutic interventions with individuals with mental retardation. *The Habilitative Mental Healthcare Newsletter, 15,* 116-119.

Reese, R. M., Sherman, J. A., & Sheldon, J. (1984). Reducing agitated-disruptive behavior of mentally retarded residents of community group homes: The roles of self-recording and peer-prompted self-recording. *Analysis and Intervention in Developmental Disabilities, 4,* 91-108.

Reiss, S. (1994). *Handhook of challenging behavior: Mental health aspects of mental retardation.* Worthington, OH: International Diagnostic Systems.

Reiss, S., & Benson, B. (1985). Psychosocial correlates of depression in mentally retarded adults: I. Minimal social support and stigmatization. *American Journal of Mental Deficiency, 89,* 331-337.

Reiss, S., & Benson, B. (1984). Awareness of negative social conditions among mentally retarded, emotionally disturbed outpatients. *American Journal of Psychiatry, 141,* 88-90.

Reiss, S., Levitan, G., & Szyszko, J. (1982). Emotional disturbance and mental retardation: Diagnostic overshadowing. *American Journal of Mental Deficiency, 86,* 567-574.

Reynolds, W.M., & Miller, K.L. (1985). Depression and learned helplessness in mentally retarded and non-mentally retarded adolescents: An initial investigation. *Applied Research in Mental Retardation, 6,* 295-306.

Richard, H.C. (1986). Relaxation training. *Psychiatric Aspects of Mental Retardation Reviews, 5,* 11-15.

Richard, H.C., Thrasher, K.A., & Elkins, P.D. (1984). Responses of persons who are mentally retarded to four components of relaxation instruction. *Mental Retardation, 22,* 248-252.

Roback, H.B., & Shelton, M. (1995). Effects of confidentiality limitations on the psychotherapeutic process. *Journal of Psychotherapy Research and Practice, 3,* 185-193.

Rogers, C.R., & Dyamond, R.F. (1954). *Psychotherapy and personality change.* Chicago: University Press.

Rosen, H. G., & Rosen, S. (1969). Group therapy as an instrument to develop a concept of self-worth in the adolescent and young adult mentally retarded. *Mental Retardation, 7,* 52-55.

Ross, D. M., & Ross, S. A. (1982). *Hyperactivity* (2nd ed.). New York: Wiley.

Rotatori, A.F., Fox, R., & Switzey, H. (1980). A parent-teacher administered weight reduction program for obese down syndrome adolescents. *Journal of Behavioral Therapy and Experimental Psychiatry, 10,* 339-341.

Rudolph, G. DeM. (1955). An experiment of group therapy with mental detectives. *International Journal of Social Psychiatry, 1,* 49-53 .

Ruesch, J., & Kees, W. (1956). *Nonverbal communication.* Los Angeles: University of California Press.

Ruth, R. (1995). Some recent trends in psychoanalysis and their relevance for treating persons with mental retardation. In A. Dosen, A. van Gennep & G. Zwanikken (Eds.), *Proceedings of the First Congress of the European Association for Mental Health in Mental Retardation. (p. 122).* Leiden, The Netherlands: Logon.

Saliga, C., Kirchner, L., & Loschen, E. (1996). Nonpharmacologic treatment of anxiety disorders: One woman's story. In A. Poindexter (Ed.), *Assessment and treatment of anxiety disorders in persons with mental retardation.* Kingston, NY: NADD Press.

Sarason, S. B. (1953). Psychotherapy. In S. Sarason (Ed.), *Psychological problems in mental deficiency* (pp. 263-330). New York: Harper & Brothers.

Scanlon, P. L. (1978). Social work with the mentally retarded client. *Social Casework, 59,* 161-166.

Schloss, P.J. (1982). Verbal interaction patterns in depressed and non-depressed institutionalized mentally retarded adults. *Applied Research in Mental Retardation, 3,* 1-12.

Schloss, P. J., Smith, M., Santora, C., & Bryant, R. (1989). A respondent conditioning approach to reducing anger responses of a dually diagnosed man with mild mental retardation. *Behavior Therapy, 20,* 459-464.

Schramski, T. (1984). Role playing as a therapeutic approach with the mentally retarded. *Psychiatric Aspects of Mental Retardation Reviews, 3,* 26-32.

Scorgie, K. I. (1996). From devastation to transformation: Managing life when a child is disabled. Doctoral thesis. University of Alberta, Edmonton, Canada.

Senatore, V., Matson, J.L., & Kazdin, A. E. (1982). A comparison of behavioral methods to train social skills to mentally retarded adults. *Behavior Therapy, 13,* 313-324.

Shapiro, E.A. (Ed.). (1997). *The inner world in the outer world: Psychoanalytic perspectives.* New Haven: Yale University Press.

Silka, V., & Hauser, M. (1997). Psychiatric assessment of the person with mental retardation. *Psychiatric Annual, 27,* 170-174.

Silvestri, R. (1977). Implosive therapy treatment of emotionally disturbed retardates. *Journal of Consulting and Clinical Psychology, 45,* 14-22 .

Simeonsson, R.J. (1988). Unique characteristics of families with young handicapped children. In D.B. Bailey & R.J. Simeonsson (Eds.), *Family assessment in early intervention (pp.* 27-43). Columbus, OH: Merrill.

Sinason, V. (1992). *Mental handicap and the human condition: New approaches from the Tavistock* London: Free Association Books.

Sletten, I., Brown, M., Evenson, R., & Altman, H. (1972). Suicide in mental hospital patients. *Diseases of the Nervous System, 33,* 328-334.

Slivkin, S.E., & Bernstein, N.R. (1967). Goal-directed group psychotherapy for retarded adolescents. *American Journal of Psychotherapy, 22,* 35-45 .

Snyder, R., & Sechrest, L. (1959). An experimental study of directive group therapy with defective delinquents. *American Journal of Mental Deficiency, 64,* 177-123.

Sobsey, D. (1996a). Rethinking parent and professional relationships. In R. Friedlander & D. Sobsey (Eds.), *Proceedings of the NADD 13th Annual Conference* (pp. 37-42). Kingston, NY: NADD Press.

Sobsey, D. (1996b). Family transformation: from dale evans to neil young. In R. Friedlander & D. Sobsey (Eds.), *Proceedings of the NADD 13th Annual Conference* (pp. 7-14). Kingston, NY. NADD Press.

Sovner, R., & Hurley, A. (1992). The diagnostic treatment formulation for psychotropic drug therapy. *The Habilitative Mental Healthcare Newsletter, 11,* 81-86.

Spano, S. (1995). Elements of family centered care. In R.J. Fletcher (Ed.), *Proceedings of the NADD Annual Conference* (pp. 13-18). Kingston, NY. NADD Press.

Stacey, C.L., DeMartino, M.F., & Sarason, S.B. (1957). *Counseling and psychotherapy with the mentally retarded. A book of readings.* Glencoe, IL. Free Press.

Stark, J. (1992). A professional and personal perspective on families. *Mental Retardation, 30,* 247-254.

Stavrakaki, C., & Klein, J. (1986). Psychotherapies with the mentally retarded. *Psychiatric Clinics of North America. 9,* 773-743.

Steinberg, P., & Garcia A. (1989). *Sociodrama: Who's in your shoes*. New York: Praeger.

Stephens, R.M., Matson, J.L., Westmoreland, T., & Kulpa, J. (1981). Modification of psychotic speech with mentally retarded patients. *Journal of Mental Deficiency Research, 25,* 187-197.

Sternlicht, M. (1977). Issues in counseling and psychotherapy with mentally retarded individuals. In I. Bialer & M. Sternlicht (Eds.), *The psychology of mental retardation: Issues and approaches* (pp. 453-490). New York: Psychological Dimensions.

Sternlicht, M. (1970). Suicidal tendencies among institutionalized retardates. *Birmingham (Eng.) Midland Society for the Study of Mental Subnormality,* 93-102.

Sternlicht, M. (1966). Psychotherapeutic procedure with the retarded. In E. Nurmad (Ed.), *International Review of Research in Mental Retardation, 10,* 279-354). New York: Academic Press.

Sternlicht, M. (1966). Treatment approaches to delinquent retardates. *International Journal of Group Psychotherapy, 16,* 91-93.

Sternlicht, M. (1965). Psychotherapy techniques useful with mentally retarded: A review and critique. *Psychiatric Quarterly, 39,* 84-90.

Sternlicht, M. (1964). Establishing an initial relationship in group psychotherapy with delinquent retarded male adolescents. *American Journal of Mental Deficiency, 69,* 39-41.

Stevenson, E.K., Hudgens, R.W., Held, C.P., Meredith, C.H., Hendrix, M.E., & Carr, D.L. (1972). Suicidal communication by adolescents. *Diseases of the Nervous System, 33,* 112-22.

Stone, D., & Coughlin, P.M. (1973). Four process variables in counseling with mentally retarded patients. *American Journal of Mental Deficiency, 77,* 408-414.

Stubblebine, J.M. (1957). Group psychotherapy with some epileptic mentally deficient adults. *American Journal of Mental Deficiency, 61*, 725-730.

Sturmey, P. (1995). Diagnostic-based pharmacological treatment of behavior disorders in persons with developmental disabilities: A review and a decision-making typology. *Research in Developmental Disabilities, 16,* 235-252.

Symington, N. (1981). The psychotherapy of a subnormal patient. *British Journal of Medical Psychology, 54*, 187-199.

Szivos, S.E., & Griffiths, E. (1990). Group processes involved in coming to terms with a mentally retarded identity. *Mental Retardation, 28*, 331-341.

Szymanski, L.S. (1980). Individual psychotherapy with retarded persons. In L. Szymanski & M. Tanguay (Eds.), *Emotional disorders of mentally retarded persons: Assessment, treatment, and consultation* (pp. 131-147). Baltimore: University Park Press.

Szymanski, L.S., & Kiernan, W.E. (1983). Multiple family group therapy with developmentally disabled adolescents and young adults. *International Journal of Group Psychotherapy, 33,* 521-534.

Szymanski, L.S., & Rosefsky, Q.B. (1980). *Group psychotherapy with retarded persons: Assessment, treatment, and consultation* (pp. 173-194). Baltimore: University Park Press.

Szymanski, L. & Tanguay, M. (1980). *Emotional disorders of mentally retarded persons.* Baltimore: University Park Press.

Teoduro, N. (1994). The three approaches to family intervention. Part I of II: The challenge of "seeing" the families of persons with disabilities. *The NADD Newsletter, 11,* 1-7. Kingston, NY: NADD Press.

Teoduro, N. (1994). The three approaches to family intervention. Part 11: On combating isolation with "family support". *The NADD Newsletter, 11,* 1-9. Kingston, NY: NADD Press.

Thompson, T., & Gray, D. B. (Eds.). (1994*). Destructive behavior in developmental disabilities: Diagnosis and treatment.* Thousand Oaks, CA: Sage.

Thorin, E., Yovanoff, P., & Irvin, L. (1996). Dilemmas faced by families during their young adults' transitions to adulthood: A brief report. *Mental Retardation, 34*, 117-120.

Thorne, F.C. (1948). Counseling and psychotherapy with mental detectives. *American Journal of Mental Deficiency, 52,* 263-271.

Tomasulo, D. (1998). *Action methods in group psychotherapy: Practical aspect.* Philadelphia: Accelerated Development: Taylor & Francis.

Tomasulo, D.J. (1997). Beginning and maintaining a group. *The Habilitative Mental Healthcare Newsletter, 16,* 41-48.

Tomasulo, D. (1994). Action techniques in group counseling: The double. *The Habilitative Mental Healthcare Newsletter, 13,* 41-45.

Tomasulo, D. (1992). *Group counseling for people with mild to moderate mental retardation/developmental disabilities: An interactive-behavioral model.* New York: Young Adult Institute.

Tomasulo, D. (1992). *Interactive-behavioral group counseling for people with mild to moderate mental retardation*.(Two videos) New York: Young Adult Institute.

Tomasulo, D., Keller, E., & Pfadt A. (1995). The healing crowd: Process, content and technique issues in group counseling for people with mental retardation. *The Habilitative Mental Healthcare Newsletter, 14,* 43-50.

Tsoi-Hoshmand, L.S. (1985). Phenomenologically based groups for developmentally disabled adults. *Journal of Counseling and Development, 64,* 147-148.

Turner, S.M., Hersen, M., & Bellack, A.S. (1978). Social skills training to teach prosocial behaviors in an organically impaired and retarded patient. *Journal of Behavior Therapy and Experimental Psychiatry, 9,* 253-258.

Vail, D.J. (1955). An unsuccessful experiment in group therapy. *American Journal of Mental Deficiency, 60,* 144-151.

Valenti-Hein, D.C. (1990). A dating skills program for adults with mental retardation.*The Habilitative Mental Healthcare Newsletter, 9,* 46-50.

Valenti-Hein, D.C. (1990). *The dating skills program: Teaching social-sexual skills to adults with mental retardation.* Worthington, OH: International Diagnostic Systems.

Virkkunen, M. (1974). Suicide linked to homicide. *Psychiatric Quarterly, 48,* 276-82.

Virkkunen, M. (1972). On suicides by disability pensioners. *Acta Soc-Med, 1,* 1-8.

Walker-Hirsch, L., & Champagne, M.P. (1992). The circles for use as a counseling strategy: An old dog learns new tricks. *The NADD Newsletter, 9,* 1-6. Kingston, NY: NADD Press.

Walters, A.S., Barrett, R.P., Knapp, L.G., & Borden, M.D. (1995). Suicidal behavior in children and adolescents with mental retardation. *Research in Developmental Disabilities, 16,* 85-96,

Walters, R.M. (1990). Suicidal behavior in severely mentally handicapped patients. *British Journal of Psychiatry, 157,* 444-446.

Waranch, H. R., Iwata, B. A., Wohl, M. K., & Nidiffer, F. D. (1981). Treatment of a retarded adult's mannequin phobia through in vivo desensitization and shaping approach responses. *Journal of Behavior Therapy and Experimental Psychiatry, 12,* 359-362.

Wehman, P., Gilson, S. F., & Tusler, A. (Eds.). (1997). Disability empowerment. [Special issue]. *Journal of Vocational Rehabilitation, 9*(1).

Wikler, L. (1981). Chronic stresses of families of mentally retarded children. *Family Relations, 30,* 281-288.

Wikler, L., Wasow, M., & Hatfield, E. (1983). Seeking strengths in families of developmentally disabled children. National Association of Social Workers, Inc. *Social Work, 28,* 313-315.

Wilcox, G.T., & Guthrie, G.M. (1957). Changes in adjustment of institutionalized female defectives following group psychotherapy. *Journal of Clinical Psychology, 13,* 9-13.

Will, M. (1993). The question of personal autonomy. *Journal of Vocational Rehabilitation, 3,* 9-10.

Williams, D. (1994) *Somebody somewhere.* New York: Random House.

Wilson, B., & Jackson, H. J. (1980). An in vivo approach to the desensitisation of a retarded child's toilet phobia. *Australian Journal of Developmental Disabilities, 6,* 137-141.

Wong, B.Y.L. (1985). Metacognition and learning disabilities. *Instructional Practices, 2*, 137-180. *www.nihn.nih.gov/research/suifact.htm,* p.6.

Yalom, I. (1995). *Group psychotherapy* (4th ed). New York: Basic Books.

Yanok, J., & Beifus, J.A. (1993). Communicating about loss and mourning: Death education for individuals with mental retardation. *Mental Retardation, 31,* 144-147.

Yepsen, L.N. (1952). Counseling the mentally retarded. *American Journal of Mental Deficiency, 57.*

Young, K.A., & O'Connor, N. (1954). Measurable effects of group psychotherapy with defective delinquents. *Journal of Mental Science, 100,* 944-952.

Zec, R., Parks, R., Gambach, J., & Vicari, S. (1992). The executive board system: An innovative approach to cognitive-behavioral rehabilitation in patients with traumatic brain injury. In C. Long & L. Ross (Eds.), *Handbook of head trauma.* New York: Plenum Press.

Zelman, A.B., Samuels, S., & Abrams, D. (1985). IQ changes in young children following intensive long term psychotherapy. *American Journal of Psychotherapy, 15,* 215-227.

Zetlin, A.G., & Turner, J.L. (1985). Transition from adolescence to adulthood: Perspectives of mentally retarded individuals and their families. *American Journal of Mental Deficiency, 89,* 570-579.

Zigler, E., & Hodapp, R. M. (1986). *Understanding mental retardation.* Cambridge: University Press.

Zigler, E., Balla, D., & Butterfield, E.C. (1968). A longitudinal investigation of the relationship between preinstitutional social deprivation and social motivation in institutionalized retardates. *Journal of Personality and Social Psychology, 10,* 437-445.

Zola, I. K. (1993). Self, identity and the naming question: Reflections on the language of disability. In M. Nagler (Ed.), *Perspectives on disability* (2nd ed., pp. 15-23). Palo Alto, CA: Health Markets Research.

Subject Index

D

E

F

G

H

I

L

M

N

O

P

R

S

Author Index

A

B

C

D

E

F

G

H

I

J

K

L

M

N

O

P

Q

R

S

T

V

W

Y

Z

NADD Press Publications

Therapy Approaches For Persons With Mental Retardation
Robert J. Fletcher, D.S.W., A.C.S.W. (Ed.), 1999

Criminal Offenders With Mental Retardation: Risk Assessment and the Continuum of Community-Based Treatment Programs
Edwin J. Mikkelsen, M.D. and Wayne J. Stelk, Ph.D., 1999

Behavioral Supports: Individual Centered Interventions
Dorothy M. Griffiths Ph.D.; William I. Gardner, Ph.D. and JoAnne Nugent, M.A. (Eds.), 1998

Assessment and Treatment of Anxiety Disorders
Ann R. Poindexter, M.D. (Ed.), 1996

Habilitative Neuropsychiatry: Psychopharmacology (1985-1986) A Reference Guide
Jeffery J. Fahs, M.D.

Look for future NADD Press publications on these related topics:

Aggression
William I. Gardner, Ph.D. (Ed.)

Psychopharmacology
Earl Loschen, M.D. (Ed.)

Program Models
John Jacobson, Ph.D. (Ed.)

Older Adults
Robert Pary, M.D. (Ed.)

Staff Training
Donna Nagy McNelis, Ph.D.

Diagnostic Manual
Earl Loschen, M.D. (Ed.)

For information about obtaining these books or information about NADD, contact:

An association for persons with developmental disabilities and mental health needs.

132 Fair St., Kingston, NY 12401-4802
Phone: (914) 331-4336 (800) 331-5362 Fax: (914) 331-4569 E-mail: thenadd@aol.com
Web site: www.thenadd.org